D. E. HARDING

THE SCIENCE OF THE 1st PERSON

Its Principles, Practice, and Potential

God made the senses turn outwards:
therefore a man looks outwards, not
into himself. Now and again a daring
soul, desiring immortality, has looked
back and found himself.
                    KATHA UPANISHAD

The second and third persons do not
appear except to the first person.
                    RAMANA MAHARSHI

By alienation is meant a mode of experience
in which the person experiences himself as
an alien. He has become, one might say,
estranged from himself. He does not
experience himself as the centre of his world...
The alienated person is out of touch with himself
as he is out of touch with any other person. He, like
the others, is experienced as things are experienced.
                    ERICH FROMM

The subject is not in the world.
                    WITTGENSTEIN

The Shollond

ISBN: 0-9534255-6-8

© D. E. Harding 1997, 2001.
All rights reserved.

Published by
The Shollond Trust
87B Cazenove Road, London N16 6BB
Tel & Fax: 020 8806 3710
email: headexchange@gn.apc.org
website: www.headless.org

The Shollond Trust is a UK charitable trust, reg. no. 1059551.

Printed and bound in Great Britain by
The Bath Press, Bath.

Affectionately dedicated to
RICHARD LANG

Also published by The Shollond Trust:

On Having No Head,
Zen and the Rediscovery of the Obvious.
D. E. Harding.

Head Off Stress,
Beyond the Bottom Line.
D. E. Harding.

Look For Yourself,
The Science and Art of Self-realisation.
D. E. Harding.

The Hierarchy of Heaven and Earth,
A New Diagram of Man in the Universe.
D. E. Harding.

Religions Of The World,
A Handbook For The Open-minded.
D. E. Harding.

The Little Book of Life and Death.
D. E. Harding.

Stepping Into Brilliant Air.
Colin Oliver.

The Science of the First Person

CONTENTS

PROLOGUE

The purpose of this book is to place in an uncompromisingly modern and Western setting the essential teaching and goal of spiritual religion - called Awakening or Enlightenment or Liberation. I aim to show how accurately this ancient, pre-scientific wisdom dovetails into the contemporary science-dominated scene, once that wisdom has been stripped of its traditional embellishments and sectarian oddities and holy language. While allowing that our modern science is valid and indeed indispensable as far as it goes, I claim that the ancient wisdom goes much further, that it is in a real sense more scientific and more sensible than science, as we know it, could ever be, and is in fact its practical and theoretical complement. In other words, I shall maintain that Western objective science is only half of real science (the other half being the science of the Subject or 1st Person) and that we are in trouble because we mistake it for the whole. Our aim here is to start correcting this mistake and to present Enlightenment in a form that the science-minded Westerner can make sense of and put into immediate practice.

First, then, let us briefly notice the procedure of ordinary science (the science of the observed, of the object or 3rd person, SCIENCE-3 for short). Then let us compare it with the procedure of its complement (the science of the observer, of the Subject or 1st Person, SCIENCE-1 for short), and go on to supply numerous illustrations of how, in detail, SCIENCE-1 rectifies and completes SCIENCE-3, 37 of them to be precise.

SCIENCE-3 -- THE SCIENCE OF THE OBSERVED
Science as we know it is concerned with the structure and behaviour of the phenomena that make up the objective universe. Its aim is to find out precisely what goes on at the various observational levels, the 'horizontal' links at each level, and the 'vertical' links between levels.

It attempts to account for the configuration of present phenomena in terms of their past, to predict their future, and to indicate (wherever possible) how they may be controlled and put to human use.

The amazing success of this procedure of SCIENCE-3 has in the past been largely due to the scientist's knack of keeping himself out of the picture. But he doesn't thereby dispose of himself. The most he does is apply his habitual objective procedure to himself as Subject, and make an object or 3rd person of himself. But this isn't being candid. He's pretending to be the very opposite of what he really is. No way can he avoid being the 1st Person that demands a science of its own.

SCIENCE-1 -- THE SCIENCE OF THE OBSERVER

This science requires its practitioner to do exactly what SCIENCE-3 forbids - to put himself back in the picture and take his subjectivity seriously. Here is a procedure so revolutionary, its subject-matter so unique, its results so remarkable, that they constitute an altogether novel kind of science. This is only to be expected. As the 1st Person is to the 3rd so are their respective sciences to each other: in every particular, SCIENCE-1 is the polar opposite of SCIENCE-3. Yet it contradicts nothing, undoes nothing. Instead, it carries to its proper conclusion the immense work already done. In no sense is it anti-scientific; rather it is ultra-scientific or meta-scientific. And its procedure is simply this: by turning his attention through 180° and viewing himself as he is to himself, SCIENTIST-1 is at last in a position to remove the basic anomalies of SCIENCE-3, and simultaneously to solve his own basic problems, the problems of life.[1]

These are bold assertions. The supporting evidence follows. But first you must qualify yourself to read on, for the Science of the 1st Person will make no sense till you see what the 1st Person is. Between pages 46 and 47 you will find a folded paper tunnel. Open it up like this:

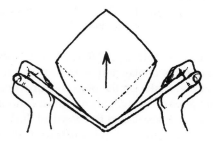

fit your face into one end of it, and hold the other up against your bathroom mirror. What you see behind glass at the far end is yourself as 3rd person, and what you see right here at the near end is yourself as 1st Person. *Could they be more different - the face there, and the Space here that's taking it in?*

Back now to our Prologue. To remind yourself of your 1st

Personhood as you read on, all you have to do is stop overlooking the Aware Emptiness that's your side of these black marks on white paper, taking them in. My asking you to do this is a reasonable requirement. To engage in a scientific discipline, while refusing to carry out any of the laboratory tests on which it is based, would be somewhat futile. In the case of SCIENCE-1 it would probably do more harm than good.

The quotations from the mystics and masters are printed as footnotes, and not in the text, in order to emphasise that they form no part of the present argument, and are certainly not cited as authoritative. They are intended only to illustrate the antiquity and universality of SCIENCE-1. SCIENTIST-1 tests the scriptures by experience, not experience by the scriptures.

[1]WITTGENSTEIN says of SCIENCE-3: *We feel that when all possible scientific questions have been answered, the problems of life remain completely untouched.*

1: SCIENCE-1 INSISTS ON VERIFICATION

The hallmark of a scientific discovery is that it is capable of independent verification; it isn't for believing on even the most eminent authority's say-so, but for doubting and testing. In practice, however, such testing is rarely as easy or as thorough as it might be, and almost never quite final; consequently much of what is taken to be the settled knowledge of SCIENCE-3 is, in fact, liable to re-examination and revision.

SCIENCE-1 is even more radical in its appeal, over the head of all authority, to first-hand experience; it exists for testing and by testing, not otherwise. It has no laurels to rest on. I may never tell you what it's like to be 1st Person where you are (I'm in no position to say) but only what it's like where I am - just in case you should happen to get similar readings. Much more than this, I may not even tell you (or myself) what it was like to be 1st Person here yesterday, or an hour or a minute ago. I can't rely even on my own authority! For if I'm seeing what's here at the Centre of my world, and not merely thinking it, it is memory-free, a brand new discovery every time. I can verify my past findings, with the rigour this most exacting SCIENCE-1 demands, only by continually bringing them up to date. In fact, the past is obsolete, ruled out. SCIENCE-1 is the science of the 1st Person singular, *present tense*, because the true 1st Person is only now: the memory and anticipation of 1st-personhood turn it into an object, into 3rd-personhood. Whereas SCIENCE-3 must lean heavily on past experience and take for granted much of its ever-growing stock of knowledge, SCIENCE-1 may take nothing for granted.

Nor can SCIENCE-1 be dismissed as a series of exercises in self-contained subjectivity, merely private experiences privately verifiable and subject to no external and objective checks. No: its findings are verifiable in public by the ordinary methods of SCIENCE-3. Not only do I tell you what's right here, namely Nothing, but I follow it up with an invitation to come here (preferably armed with the proper instruments) and discover for yourself whether I am speaking the truth. And then, if you accept my invitation, don't you leave behind your view of me as a man, as a face, as a patch of skin, as cells, as molecules, as atoms, and so on, and come eventually to a place where you make practically nothing of me -

just as I told you? It's true that you can't quite get here where I am, but remain (however close) an outside observer, with the result that you don't empty me entirely. You have to leave that last step to me; but it is the obvious conclusion of all the steps you have taken towards me.[1]

[1]LEWIS CARROL: *THROUGH THE LOOKING GLASS: 'I think I'll go and meet her,' said Alice… 'You can't possibly do that', said the Rose. 'I should advise you to walk the other way.' This sounded nonsense to Alice, so she said nothing, but set off at once towards the Red Queen. To her surprise, she lost sight of her in a moment.*
THE KORAN: You are like a mirage in the desert, which the thirsty man thinks is water; but when he comes up to it he finds it is nothing. And where he thought it was, there he finds God.

2: SCIENCE-1 IS ULTRA-ANALYTIC

SCIENCE-3 doesn't go by appearances but looks into things. It takes them to pieces to find out what they are really made of, what makes them go. Clearly the particles or wavicles, or quarks or sub-quarks, into which the physicist has (so far) resolved bodies, aren't the end; while anything remains, however shadowy, there arises the question of its composition. He still stands at a distance from his material and by no means penetrates to the thing-in-itself, to the heart of the matter: the underlying whatever-it-is stays as inscrutable as ever.

But when he turns his attention round and examines himself as 1st Person, when he becomes his own unique sample of what-ever-it-is, when he takes seriously that one collection of particles concerning which he has inside information and upon which he is the sole and final authority, then he completes his work of reduction and observes that in the last analysis it is absolutely empty - yet aware of itself as empty: formless - yet well informed on the subject: qualityless - yet tickled to death at the fact.[1] *He sees that the Reality behind appearances is No-thing seeing itself as no-thing.* Or rather, he sees that the Reality 'behind' appearances is in fact *in front* of them, taking them in, and is none other than himself as 1st Person. The tunnel experiment which you have just done will make this per-fectly clear.

[1]*THE SECRET OF THE GOLDEN FLOWER: If a man wants to make certain of his body, he cannot get at it... In this kind of seeing, one only sees that no shape is here.*
HEART SUTRA: Here, form is void.
TAULER: Unform thyself.

3: SCIENCE-1 IS ULTRA-SYNTHETIC

B ut analysis is only the descending half of the scientific escalator. The opposite aim of synthesis, the discovery and study of increasingly comprehensive 'gestalten' and 'ecological units', and ultimately of a complete ascending series of inorganic and organic and supra-organic wholes (severed from which their parts or organs or functions remain more-or-less inexplicable) - this aim also is becoming a respectable and important function of SCIENCE-3. (For instance, the climate, soil, flora and fauna of a tropical rain-forest are found to be so interdependent that they can be understood only as a supra-biological whole, just as - at a lower level - the leaves and branches and roots of one of its trees can be understood only as a biological whole. Indeed it is a mark of a real whole that it sports qualities and functions that can't be found in its parts. Each new level displays its own unique, unpredictable 'emergents'.)

This indispensable work of putting-things-together-again must however fall far short of its goal (which is the discovery of the all-inclusive and only true Whole) so long as the scientist declines to add himself in. How could he find this unity while he poses as an observing *thing* standing over against the totality of observed things, thereby dividing the One into two? When at last, however, he sees this observing thing to be No-thing, but the Ground or empty Container of all the things that confront it, they are now *all there*; he sees them as *one* filling, as a Universe, no matter how mutually incongruous they might seem apart from him. Disappearing as one object facing a miscellany of objects, SCIENTIST-1 reappears as the solitary subject who holds together all objects in the perfect synthesis.[1] The 1st Person becomes truly Nothing by handing over everything to the Whole, which thereby becomes truly All, for its vital missing part is now restored.

This needs trying out. Let me first see What I am, then how this unifies things, then what is the 'emergent quality' of the synthesis.

---

[1]ECKHART: *As long as I am this or that, I am not all things.*
RAMANA MAHARSHI: *The trouble arises when one says, 'I am this or that'. Be yourself, that is all.*

13

4: SCIENCE-1 IS MATHEMATICALLY PRECISE

So long as naturalists were content to compile illustrated catalogues of Nature they remained collectors rather than scientists. Indeed the progress of SCIENCE-3 has largely consisted in the development of its toolkit, in the gradual replacement of primitive and very blunt verbal-pictorial instruments by razor-like mathematical ones. Even so, there are wide areas of study (notably in the sciences of life) whose language-tools are still largely anecdotal and descriptive; and in no area does the abstract language of mathematics altogether take care of the concrete phenomena. The mathematics of SCIENCE-3 - the science of the observed - is bound always to fall far short of its own ideal precision and applicability.

Not so the mathematics of SCIENCE-1, the science of the observer. Consider enumeration or counting. There are three methods - the childish, the grown-up, and the childlike. (a) The small child in a room with, say, 4 people, and not counting himself at all, reckons 4 faces. (b) The grown-up, miscounting himself as object 1 (or more politely as object 5), reckons 5. (c) The childlike 1st Person, again, reckons 4, because he neither (like the small child) overlooks himself as Subject nor (like the grown-up) classes himself with objects. He sees that he's neither a grown-up nor a child, that he has never begun to grow up into anything whatever, so he counts himself *out* as a thing and *in* as No-thing, as Zero.
He always starts counting from nought.

(a) Childish	1 2 3 4	not counting oneself at all
(b) Grown-up SCIENCE-3	1 2 3 4 5	miscounting Subject as object 1
	5 1 2 3 4	miscounting Subject as object 5
(c) Childlike SCIENCE-1	0 1 2 3 4	counting oneself as Subject 0

Whatever SCIENTIST-1 (c) classes together for counting - whether eyes, faces, heads, men, bodies or things of any sort, persons, ideas, qualities - he is aware of himself as nothing like that, not in the same class at all. He sees that, as 1st Person, he is no more to be added in with them than the fruit-bowl with the fruit. The 1st Person is Zero in respect of all existents - essential to the operation of counting them but uninvolved, unclassifiable, their uncountable and unaccountable Counter. SCIENTIST-3, on the other hand, thinks of himself as a thing among things, an object among objects, a number to be added in at the end of the series if not at the beginning. His world, divided into this observing thing and those observed things, is two worlds. So it happens that, while SCIENTIST-3 sorts out many secondary problems, he aggravates the primary one, which is the problem of duality, the alienation of self from non-self, with all its attendant anxieties.[1]

SCIENCE-3 has a very elaborate mathematical toolkit, SCIENCE-1 a very simple one, namely Zero - myself as Nothing or number 0 instead of number one. All that, as SCIENTIST-3, I supposed I had subtracted from the world, I now, as SCIENTIST-1, add back, leaving Zero here and Unity there. Repeating the tunnel experiment - with my own face at the far end of it, with another's there, with the world as it now presents itself - I make sure of getting the sum right. Looking simultaneously out at the observed and in at the observer, instead of $1 \longleftrightarrow 2$ ...... I find $0 \longleftrightarrow 1$ ......

This is the ideally precise and absolutely universal formula or 'general expression for solving problems' - not merely the basic problem of duality, but as a consequence all others too. Whatever the problem, it is now all of it out there (in the 1...) and none of it in here (in the 0), and this placing of it is its radical solution. Indeed the true 1st-Person life is nothing else than the continual testing of this problem-solving formula. The reports agree that it proves itself while under test, and never while taken for granted.

[1]*KATHA UPANISHAD: Tell the mind there is but One; he who divides the One wanders from death to death.*
BRIHADARANYAKA UPANISHAD: Where there are two there is fear.

5: SCIENCE-1 IS SENSE-BASED

Modern science began as a revolt against thinking, in favour of looking - a revolt aimed at that undisciplined mediaeval intellectualism which theorised endlessly about things without getting down to observing them patiently and impartially. SCIENCE-3 appeals in the last resort not to concepts but to percepts, and upon this safe foundation alone has it succeeded in rearing its towering superstructure - which can then afford to dwarf and overshadow even the mediaeval Schoolmen's speculative designs. All the same, SCIENCE-3 must forever fall short of total humility in front of the evidence. It can't help theorising. For the scientist is blind when confronted by raw Nature unless he has some preconceptions, some idea of what to look for, some schema to fill in, or set of categories to structure what is merely given. The observed data make little impact till they are related to some tentative theory or some as-yet-unverified speculation. In short, though bare observation is basic it isn't nearly enough - for SCIENCE-3.

For SCIENCE-1 it is everything. The Void here cannot be guessed at or thought about or speculated on or even understood; but only perceived. Thinking about it destroys it by giving it content.[1] Here, then, is the meta-science which, if it is to function at all, can never get away from its sense-basis, its sure foundation of ultra-radical empiricism. It cannot so much as glimpse its material (which is the scientist-in-himself) while it is blinkered by any preconception or theory or philosophy or dogma. All that is needed, all that is permitted, is simple openness, bare attention. As a result, its findings are undistorted, given and not cooked up, self-evident: that is to say, truly scientific.

Compared with SCIENCE-1, SCIENCE-3 is sense-handicapped. For example, though stars and galaxies can be seen (and occasionally heard), they certainly can't be smelled or tasted or touched; and subatomic particles can't even be seen. What SCIENCE-1 studies, on the other hand, is equally accessible to all the senses. Its procedure isn't just two-way looking, but also two-way hearing, two-way tasting, two-way smelling... Just as I now *see* here, in front of this page and this hand, Nothing (total absence of shape, structure, limits, opacity, colour, movement), so I now *hear*, this side of the sounds (birdsong, car-noises, children shouting) that are coming and going in it, Silence. Equally I now *smell* here, thankfully, no trace of tobacco smoke or cooking or drains... Thus this 1st Person is illuminated by *every* sense, as the unchanging and indispensable foreground of all these ever-changing sensations. In my exploration of *others* I use what senses are available, as best I can; in my exploration of *Myself* I use them all - to perfection. What is here to go wrong?

[1]HUANG-PO: *The ignorant reject what they see, not what they think; the wise reject what they think, not what they see.*
SIMEON THE NEW THEOLOGIAN: *O Lord, to me you are wholly visible, and your substance is fused with my nature.*

6: THE FINDINGS OF SCIENCE-1 ARE INDUBITABLE

It is very possible - indeed necessary - to have doubts about what I see *there*. (Thus I'm sure I'm now seeing something I provisionally call a spot of light, but what it is that looks like this I'm not sure; it is probably a star, but then it could be a galaxy or a planet or a UFO or a satellite or a meteorological balloon or a firefly on the window, or even the product of liver trouble.) But it is impossible for me to doubt what I see *here*, namely the *Absence* of any spot of light, of any colour or shape or motion, of anything whatever. In this instance there is no question of interpretation, for there is nothing to interpret. The Void here is itself and not an appearance of something else; it doesn't point elsewhere or call for explanation or elucidation. What it visibly is it really is. How unlike the data which SCIENTIST-3 investigates, data that aren't at all what they seem! In fact, his job is never to take them at their face value, always to question and look beyond what he finds. Only this motionless and colourless No-shape, which is the investigator himself as 1st Person, is wholly indubitable and unproblematic. The One who is it knows what to make of it. The only 'thing' that can safely be taken at its face value is one's own faceless Nothingness. Everything else is at least two-faced and by its very nature deceptive.[1]

[1]CHUANG-TZU: *What I call perfection of vision is not seeing others, but oneself.*
SHEN-HUI: *Seeing into one's Self-nature is seeing into Nothingness. Seeing into Nothingness is true seeing and eternal seeing.*

7: THE FINDINGS OF SCIENCE-1 ARE UNMEDIATED

Another of the disabilities of SCIENCE-3 is that, because the observer is always stationed at a distance from his material, he has to rely on a third party or go-between of dubious character, a fallible transport system, a medium which is certainly very different from the message. Such is light - that intricate system of wave-motions in space, further complicated by atmosphere, water-vapour, dust, ionised particles, and so on - with the result that what arrives *chez* SCIENTIST-3 is at the very best an older and travel-stained version of what set out. How to make allowance for every scar, every mark of the journey and every vehicle-produced distortion, how to work back from what presents itself here and now, to what it originally was over there a millionth of a second ago, or perhaps a million years ago? Can they in any sense be the *same*? Of course SCIENTIST-3 makes allowances for some of the grosser distortions due to the medium, but is obliged to take the general purport of the message on trust. The ideal medium, the only real safeguard against distortion, would be no medium at all, observed and observer coinciding and leaving no room for error in the transmission of information from one to the other. Only SCIENCE-1, where object and Subject unite, conforms to this ideal, or comes anywhere near it.[1]

---

[1]HSU-YUN: *Who is it that repeats the Buddha's name? We should try to find out where this 'Who' comes from and what it looks like.*
RUYSBROECK: *The loving contemplative, in his Ground wherein he rests, sees and feels nothing but an incomprehensible Light; and through that simple Nudity which enfolds all things, he finds himself, and feels himself, to be that same Light by which he sees, and nothing else.*
WU-MEN: *Let subject and object be so oned that the wind cannot pass between them.*

8: SCIENCE-1 DISCOVERS THE REAL

In fact, *any* distance, *any* medium coming between the object and its observer, no matter how shallow and clear it may be, does much more than refract and distort and cloud: the native reality is entirely re-modelled into some acquired appearance, some distant effect which is quite unlike its cause. (Thus you don't have two human faces - an apparent one presented to me here, duplicating a real one there of your own - but only this apparent one, as I find when I move up to you and lose it: evidently, then, your Reality is nothing like your appearance. And this is verifiably true of all the things around us: they vanish on close inspection.) And indeed - unlike common sense - SCIENCE-3 admits to being the science of phenomena and not noumena, of regional appearances and not their central Reality, of the way things look and not the way they are. It is the science of the relative, of how things happen to strike the observer, whose position and motion make all the difference. It is the science of what seems to be, of the endlessly variegated enchantments which distance lends to the plain truth.

SCIENCE-1, on the other hand, is the disenchanting science of what *is*, of the Real, of where appearances come from and what they are appearances of. *Its practitioner is careful to select for his material - literally, for his subject-matter - only what he can get right up to and into, and so know intimately, and treats the rest as sub-standard.* Accordingly he takes himself seriously as the one accessible sample of how things really are. He takes the Spot he occupies seriously as the one place he has ever really visited, the only country that is for him mirage-free and unenchanted. Here at last all is plain and straightforward, appearance and Reality come to the same thing, and what the scene looks like is exactly what it is.[1]

[1]HEIDEGGER: *No age has known so much, so many different things, about man as ours, no age has known less than ours what he is.*
RUMI: *When thou hast broken and destroyed thine own form, thou hast learned to break the form of everything.*
ECKHART: *If I knew myself as intimately as I ought, I should have perfect knowledge of all creatures.*
BRIHADARANYAKA UPANISHAD: *When the Self is seen, heard, thought of, known, everything is known.*

9: SCIENCE-1 IS NON-INTERFERING

Not only is SCIENCE-3 unfitted to examine Reality itself, but even, to a less degree, the appearances of Reality; for the discoveries of this science are made at the expense of the facts. It gets to know its material by interfering with it. Thus the presence of the social scientist in the social situation alters that situation; his evident interest in people's behaviour causes them to change their behaviour; his personality and the wording of his questions will have much to do with the answers he gets. Thus the only way the biologist can obtain a clear picture of certain cell-structures is to kill and stain the cell, with the result that he is, in part, studying his own artefact. Thus the only way the physicist can obtain information about certain particles is to hit them with other particles, thereby upsetting the information he is after.

The phenomena studied by SCIENCE-3 are necessarily to some degree unknowable because any thorough investigation of them does them violence. It isn't so much that SCIENCE-3 is ham-fisted as that its materials are vague and shy and shifting - and indeed shifty, as befits phenomena.[1] The only remedy is to turn from the unreliable to the reliable, from the observed object to the observing Subject, to that one laboratory where the scientist and his material are on really good terms, where they are so at one that neither can harm the other, and anyhow there remains Nobody to injure and Nothing to be injured.[2] Here alone is non-violent knowledge, which means genuine knowledge. Here alone the scientist finally tracks down the virgin Datum, the unmanipulated Fact, discovers it to be nothing else than himself as 1st Person singular, and becomes at last thoroughly scientific.

[1]RUMI: *Knowledge of the world is a kind of ignorance.*

[2]ECKHART: *Anything, however small, adhering to the soul, prevents your seeing me.*

10: SCIENCE-1 IS OBJECTIVE

In its pure form, SCIENCE-3 has total objectivity for its ideal. It aims at complete detachment and open-mindedness, the whole truth impartially surveyed and interpreted; and surely the results suggest that it doesn't altogether fail in this lofty aim. But inevitably it doesn't succeed either, for four main reasons. First (as we have seen) SCIENTIST-3 concerns himself only with the object's appearances and not with the Reality they are appearances of; second, he concerns himself with only a small selection from the infinity of those appearances and ignores the rest; third, even the selected appearances are (again, as we have seen) upset by his observational techniques and so partially falsified; fourth (and worst of all) he takes account only of the variable and more-or-less inscrutable half of each scientific occasion - the observed - and overlooks the constant half - the observer himself as 1st Person, who as such is real and no appearance, and is indeed the only reliable ingredient in the experimental or observational set-up.

Conversely, inasmuch as SCIENCE-1 concerns itself with the real, the constant, it is wholly realistic and reliable: oddly enough, it is the science of the Subject that is altogether objective, which means altogether scientific. Nor is this objectivity of a Pickwickian sort, only to be had by ignoring objects. On the contrary, SCIENCE-1 cheerfully recognises and values (and in a sense includes) SCIENCE-3, for it takes into account not only the seer but the seen, not only the central Reality but the nest of all its appearances. To put it another way, the Emptiness it views is marvellously filled and by no means merely empty; Subject finds itself replete with object, Observer with observed, and they are one.[1] Or, to put it differently again, whereas SCIENTIST-3 looks out, SCIENTIST-1 looks both in and out simultaneously - in at the near and out at the far, in at Who's looking and out at what's being looked at, and *only this two-way looking is fully objective.*

Some have actually tried this. They declare that, when two-way looking is persisted in, the external world is much more truly and vividly seen than when it is viewed by itself and as if it were the whole story, as if it were unobserved. It must be added, nevertheless, that even this enlightened way of looking at the world doesn't begin to perfect one's knowledge of the world, whose very nature is that it can only be inspected piecemeal and never comprehensively. Only its Source is given all-at-once and can be viewed unselectively, with complete objectivity.[2]

[1]ECKHART: *If the Soul would stay within, she would have everything.*

[2]ST. JOHN OF THE CROSS: *Only God can be perfectly known because only God is perfectly simple.*
RAMANA MAHARSHI: *Phenomena are real when experienced as the Self, but illusory when seen apart from the Self.*

11: SCIENCE-1 IS THE DISCOVERY
OF THE KNOWABLE

Only the uncomplicated is knowable. Directly any complication is introduced there comes along with it the opportunity - the necessity - for an infinite regress of study and re-interpretation: each new development (and indeed each new thinker) involves the re-assessment of what already exists, and the last word is never said about anything. And obviously any ordinary object, such as my hand or my face, is strictly inscrutable, for a thorough survey of its texture and configuration and colouring (not to mention the many levels of its microscopic structure) would take a lifetime; and could not, indeed, hope to keep pace with the ravages which time is continually inflicting upon the object. Nature won't stay still enough to have her photo taken; she is much too elusive to be tied down, much too abundant to be got into any library or laboratory. SCIENCE-3 has no choice but to over-simplify and compress the data, and rest content with bringing out some of the more significant regularities which structure Nature's infinite variety. Even so, the strait-jacketed, schematic, and largely symbolic universe of SCIENCE-3, and the regularities or 'laws' which 'govern' it, remain extremely complicated. Moreover there is always the question how far these 'laws' are valid discoveries of the scientist and how far they are mere conventions imposed by him; and always there is the certainty that they aren't final.

The knowledge in which SCIENCE-1 deals is of a totally different order, absolute and not relative, ideally transparent, all-at-once, perfectly apprehended in a moment. Foolishly I imagine I can see what I'm looking at and not what I'm looking out of, my face over there in the mirror and not my facelessness here, at this end of the tunnel. The fact is I can see clearly, can know thoroughly, *only* this Simplicity here, where there is nothing to get muddled about, or to need bringing up to date, or to relate to something or other. In short, only Self-knowledge is true knowledge.[1]

[1]D. T. SUZUKI: *All-knowledge is what constitutes the essence of Buddha-hood. It does not mean that the Buddha knows every individual thing, but that he has grasped the fundamental principle of existence and that he has penetrated deep down into the Centre of his own being.*
J. C. BRADLEY: *If anything could be called intrinsically unknowable, it is man.*

12: SCIENCE-1 IS SELF-RIGHTING

SCIENCE-1 has built into it an invaluable safety-catch or self-righting device - which SCIENCE-3 lacks altogether. It isn't that I *could* be wrong about the object out there but that to some extent I *must* be wrong: to apprehend it at all is to misapprehend it. And conversely, it isn't that I'm *likely* to be right about the bare Subject here but that I *must* be right; to see it at all is to see it perfectly as it was and is and shall be for ever and ever, exactly as all its viewers have seen it and will see it.[1] Since there is Nothing to see I cannot see half of it, nor can I half see it; this is an all-or-nothing (all-*and*-Nothing) discovery which removes any anxiety lest my Enlightenment should be dimmer than yours, or less mature, or deficient in any way whatsoever. To see this one perfect Sight is perfect Sight-seeing, therefore among those who enjoy it there can be no élite, no pecking-order - while the seeing lasts. In this sense SCIENCE-1 is ideally democratic and egalitarian. Indeed it is self-protected against every sort of abuse; either it works perfectly or not at all. How different from SCIENCE-3 which, lacking built-in safety devices, is always running hot or threatening to break down! In fact, it is when this SCIENCE-3 is at its most creative that it is most liable to doubts, anxieties, personal rivalries, and often bitter disputes.

[1]ST. JOHN OF THE CROSS: *That thou mayest know everything, seek to know nothing.*
HUANG-PO: *Only have no mind of any kind; this is known as undefiled knowledge.*

13: SCIENCE-1 REACHES AGREEMENT

However arrived at, the findings of SCIENCE-3 don't generally remain matters of opinion or heated debate. If all goes well, they are so lucidly presented and so readily tested that reasonable men everywhere tend to agree about them. Whatever the scientist's nationality, politics, religion, race, philosophical outlook, or temperament, he is likely to accept as beyond dispute a great deal of physics and chemistry (for example) and their practical applications. On the other hand, there are fields (psychology and sociology are notorious instances) where there are almost as many schools of thought as creative workers, and virtually no accepted principles. The truth is that about the *observed* there is always room for some difference of opinion, of emphasis, of approach, and it is in fact this latitude which makes the whole vast enterprise of SCIENCE-3 possible.

But about the *Observer* there can be no difference of opinion, for there is nothing to disagree about.[1] The one subject on which all must concur is, precisely, the One Subject, the 1st Person singular, present tense, in whom we are at one because we are One. This is a marvellous antidote to the terrors of an unknown and alien universe, whether science-fictional or science-factual; it shepherds Home the entire cosmic herd; it is the universal eirenicon. However prehistoric and uncouth the enjoyer of 1st-Personhood might appear, or (conversely) however ahead of ourselves in the evolutionary story, however far-flung he is in sidereal space, however fantastically non-human, however incompatible with ours his civilisation and religion and SCIENCE-3 - all discovery and enjoyment of this perennial and universal Fact is discovery of the same thing by the same Discoverer, and even a syllable of disagreement is impossible.

[1]YUNG-CHIA HSUAN-CHUEH: *Like the empty sky it has no boundaries, yet it is right in this place, ever profound and clear.*
ECKHART: *Into the soul's essence no speck can ever fall.*

14: SCIENCE-1 IS GRATIS

S CIENCE-1 reconciles all its practitioners throughout the cosmos (however many their eyes and antennae and legs, and wherever they grow them!), because What each sees himself to be is exactly What every other sees himself to be, and What they all actually are. SCIENCE-1 is the discovery that, in the last resort, there is only one Scientist, and the ultimate Science is his own in-seeing - his very own, and scot-free.

SCIENCE-3 is a costly undertaking requiring investment in huge quantities of valuable apparatus and special buildings and services, manned by armies of highly-paid experts; even so, troubles are many and an adequate return cannot be guaranteed. Moreover the more fundamental the research the more expensive it is apt to prove; to investigate 'ultimate' particles on the one hand and spiral nebulae on the other - to penetrate towards the smallest and the largest - very advanced equipment and very subtle techniques and very sophisticated thinking are needed. The truth-barrier gets harder and harder to penetrate.

To break clean through the barrier, SCIENTIST-1 has only to be himself.[1] To finish the job so laboriously and expensively pros-ecuted by SCIENCE-3, and actually to arrive at the smallest and the largest, he is already and by birthright perfectly equipped; he requires Nothing - not even that perfect infra-electron microscope, the paper tunnel, cheap though it is. To reach the ultimate depth and height he needs no step-ladder, for he has never been anywhere else. It is only what is remote that takes time and money and trouble to get to.

[1] *THE SECRET OF THE GOLDEN FLOWER: It is as if, in the middle of one's being, there were a non-being… The Confucians call it the Centre of Emptiness.*
RUMI: *When a man is awakened, he melts and perishes.*

15: SCIENCE-1 IS SIMPLE

Again, to get *almost* to the heart of things I need not only time and money and gear, but unusual intellectual gifts plus long training; whereas to get *quite* there I need none of these, no expertise at all. On the contrary, the essential qualification is that I drop all my qualifications, my hard-won knowledge and skills, and become what intrinsically I am - perfectly simple, a fool. Cleverness is precisely what prevents me from seeing what it's like here, from being myself and quite natural. So it isn't the sophisticated SCIENTIST-3 who arrives at the goal of science, but the childlike or even idiotic SCIENTIST-1, who takes the trouble to notice that he is in fact there already. This means that the most ordinary of men, however ignorant and untrained, can be a superb scientist and the world's most eminent expert on what matters most. All he has to do is look.[1]

[1]JESUS: *Unless you turn round and become like little children, you will not enter the kingdom of heaven.*
ECKHART: *God is not seen except by blindness, nor known except by ignorance, nor understood except by fools.*
LAO-TZU: *The Sage all the time sees and hears no more than an infant sees and hears.*
ST. THOMAS AQUINAS: *Nothing can be more simple than God, either in reality or in our way of understanding.*

16: SCIENCE-1 IS UNSPECIALISED

Traditionally, the authentic philosopher-scientist takes all the knowledge of his time as his province; and until a century or two ago this ideal sometimes came near to realisation.[1] And indeed, if a scientist is 'one who knows', then the more comprehensive his knowledge the more of a scientist he is. But in that case the progress of SCIENCE-3 has been the regress of SCIENTIST-3, who can no longer hope to keep up with much more than his own chosen speciality. So vast is the material and so rapid its growth that no chemist (say) or biologist or psychologist has time to skim through all the periodical literature of his own subject, let alone cover the subject in his work. Practically his only chance of making an original discovery is to confine his attention to (say) one particular kind of molecule or organism or disease, or one particular psychological condition or therapeutic technique. The result is that, though SCIENCE-3 does exist in all its magnificent range and complexity, it doesn't exist for any one scientist; it arrives in pieces and *cannot be put together:* there is no conspectus. Strictly speaking, it is incomprehensible, and its practitioners are less and less scientists in the original sense. The more it succeeds in detail the more it fails as a whole.

SCIENTIST-1 pushes specialisation to the utmost limit, thereby reversing it. He knows, not - like SCIENTIST-3 - more and more about less and less, but everything about Nothing. He stands no risk of narrow-mindedness, for his Subject-matter is boundless; he cannot concentrate on part of it, for it has no parts. To practise SCIENCE-1 at all is to practise all of it. In short, the answer to the problem of specialisation is to take another look at the specialist - from inside. He can safely and cheerfully restrict his attention to the narrowest of research projects, provided he doesn't lose touch with himSelf, with the Researcher whose breadth is infinite.

---

[1]In Aristotle in the ancient world, for instance, and in such men as Descartes, Francis Bacon, Leibniz, Pascal, and Herbert Spencer in the modern world.

17: SCIENCE-1 HAS NO COMMUNICATION PROBLEM

One of the structural weaknesses of SCIENCE-3 is the fact that the build-up of knowledge involves the breakdown of the means of conveying it; internal communications tend to seize up. The specialist is unaware of much work being done in other fields (but potentially relevant to his own field) because, besides lacking the skills and the time for wide exploration, he lacks also the jargon. To the extent that each scientific province develops its own language, he grows out of touch and tongue-tied.[1]

SCIENCE-1 has no internal communication problem. Here, information passes intact and undistorted - what is there to go wrong? When A points out the Void to B, if B sees it at all he sees it exactly as A does. And for this purpose, moreover, words prove surprisingly apt. The language which is so inadequate for the purposes of SCIENCE-3 turns out to be beautifully adequate for those of SCIENCE-1. In addition, it is full of profound hints, of such inspired double-talk as 'I am Nothing, have Nothing, want Nothing, know Nothing, am obsessed by Nothing, rely on Nothing, believe in Nothing...' It's as if language had been set up by the Nothing for itself, and the mere things that flow from the Nothing had to take their linguistic chance. Thus the more I speak of my thoughts and feelings - and specially my spiritual or mystical experiences - the more likely they are to evaporate, till in the end all is falsified and I don't know what I'm talking about; whereas the more I speak of *Where* those thoughts and feelings come from the more consistently I see what I mean and mean what I see, and the more lucidly I express it. This Source never shines more brightly than when it is being pointed out to another (really it is pointing Itself out to Itself), and then language is at its best. It is astonishing how this seeing facilitates verbal flow and precision (so that the tongueless speaker himself may listen with something like awe), and a quality of conversation which makes the average social intercourse sound like a string of interrupted monologues. And indeed some of the world's very greatest literature is similarly inspired. It is no accident that the poetry of Rumi and St. John of the Cross, and the prose of Eckhart and Traherne, should in their respective languages be pre-eminent; or that it should be Shakespeare himself who likens to an angry ape the man who is 'most ignorant of what he's most assured, his glassy essence'. The words that proceed from the conscious absence of that ape-like head come straight from the pellucid Essence itself, so it isn't surprising they should prove words of power, fit for pointing back to their transparent, mouthless Speaker. It is only What talk comes from that will bear much talking about.[2]

For good measure, not only does SCIENCE-1 have a way with words but also with forms: it possesses its own gallery of spatial diagrams or atlas of maps which greatly help communication by displaying all-at-once what words take time to say. Such is our mandala, or onion-pattern, essentially a nest of concentric circles about a centre: the centre is the 1st Person and the circles are the system of its regional appearances as 3rd person, of its manifesta-tion to observers whose distance determines the status - human or non-human - of what they observe. Such, again, is our pyramid of wholes and parts, with the Whole (or the 1st Person as All) for apex, "ultimate matter" (or the 1st Person as Nothing) for base, and man half way between.

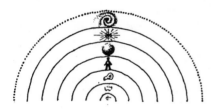
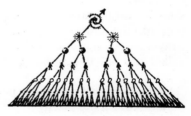

Appearances of the Real   Parts of the Whole

Though a map is no substitute for the territory, it does bear some resemblance to it. Only of onomatopoeic words like *hiss* and *plop* and *hum* can as much be said. Most are unrelated to what they stand for. The *word* 'I' is no more the *experience* of 'I' than the word 'red' is tinted red. Notoriously, words become substitutes for their meaning. This is tragically true when they are about my 1st-personhood. Talking and reading and writing about Who I am, without seeing Who I am, is a well-worn escape route from Who I am. A few minutes devoted to an experiment that re-directs my attention to the Spot I occupy (traversing our paper tunnel, for example) are worth a lifetime of centrifugal study and talk. A typical 'laboratory' or 'workshop' with (say) ten to thirty participants and lasting from three hours to several days, may try a score of such experiments, all of which have one aim - the ever-renewed discovery, from as many angles as possible, of the 1st Person Singular.[3] In a successful 'laboratory' there is no communication problem, because there are no separate communicators. And certainly there is no distinction between practised seers and novices, and no teaching but only the enjoyment of shared identity - of the 1st Person Singular awaking to the 1st Person Singular.[4]

[1]The chequered story of the discovery of DNA shows how far communication between disciplines is still possible; and also the difficulties under which a fragmented science works.

[2]Hence the tendency of in-lookers - so odd, even perverse, to the onlooker - endlessly to explore their Transparency together. Though there's Nothing to say, how they do go on about it, for at last each sees into the other's infinite depths! This true intimacy, this healing conversation, is indescribably satisfying because, in fact, here is one Talker and one Listener, and they are the same.

[3]Detailed suggestions about laboratories or workshops can be obtained from the publishers of this book.

[4]GEORGE MACDONALD: *In God alone can man meet man.*

18: SCIENCE-1 SHOWS HOW LANGUAGE SUPPORTS DELUSION

Language is venal. In the service of the truth of the 1st Person, it points to the 1st Person: witness this essay. In the service of the fictions of the 3rd person, of common sense and social convenience, it hides the 1st Person under a thick verbal smoke-screen. This is only to be expected; for the origin and development of speech and writing, alike in the history of the race and of the individual, coincide with the origin and development of the basic human delusion - the delusion that the 1st Person is unreal. Language is party to this delusion or confidence trick, which its structure and usage in every way promote. That is why sages have said that we shall find the truth when we become like infants who haven't learnt to talk.

They said it at some length, eloquently! In this Section we, too, use language to expose and correct its basic fallacy.

(a) Language ignores the 1st Person
Take the statement 'Jack sees Jill'. It seems to make sense as it stands, to be all there. But in fact it is incomplete, an abstraction. It dodges the question of who makes the statement, and on what grounds. Corrected, the statement reads: 'I see (think/imagine/believe/say...) Jack sees Jill.'

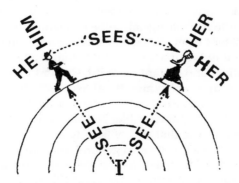

For in fact the sentence 'Jack sees Jill' doesn't happen in a vacuum or a nowhere; it is spaced out there in my universe, in what

I call its human region or onion-layer: it is a *segmental* sentence. As such, it implies the *radial* sentence 'I see...', proceeding from the Core of the onion here to the layer out there. The completed sentence 'I see Jack sees Jill' is radial-segmental. It takes account of the two-way looking of SCIENCE-1.

SCIENCE-3 is based on one-way looking, on merely segmental sentences like 'Jack sees Jill', which ignore their radial counterpart - as though there could be heads there without a no-head here, sentences without a speaker, science without a scientist! Misled by the abstractions of language into discounting the 1st Person altogether, SCIENTIST-3 *imagines* himself to be a tiny, late, accidental, lonely, superfluous thing in an alien universe. Waking from this nightmare, SCIENTIST-1 *sees* himself to be endless capacity for the universe of things, replete with all its space-time, one with all its inhabitants, and indispensable.

(b) Language plays the 1st-Person plural trick

The trickiest confidence trick we ever played on ourselves is precisely the word 'we'. *There is no 1st Person plural.* I can reasonably lump myself together with Jack and Jill only if I am something like them, and I'm not remotely like them. I have never hunted down this famous but fabulous monster called 'we'; I have never so much as glimpsed the tail of this impossible hybrid.[1]

When I say 'I see Jack' and 'Jack sees Jill' I naturally assume that the word *see* carries the same meaning in both sentences. So I twist the facts to fit the language. I *observe* Jill to be distinct and distant from Jack, and face-to-face with him in symmetrical relationship; and go on to *imagine* myself to be in a similar situation - distinct and distant from Jill, face-to-face with her, in symmetrical relationship. But in fact it's not like that at all. There's *no* observer given here distinct and distant from Jill; she and I are face-to-*no*-face, and the set-up is *not* symmetrical. No wonder I'm tricked, when the same word is used in two such contrasting senses. No wonder I think I must, here, be like Jack and Jill over there - must be that sort of 'seer' doing that sort of 'seeing'.

It is the same with verbs in general; they are hiddenly duplex, split down the middle, forced to carry opposite meanings. Take some more instances. 'We three - Jack and Jill and I - are tasting our soup' really means: 'Soup is going into those two heads and it *doesn't* taste; soup is going into this No-head and it *does* taste'. 'I saw

Jack walking in the country, and followed him' really means 'I saw Jack moving through the country, which paid no attention whatever to him. Then I saw the country moving through me - all of it, and at many different rates: the clouds and hills slowly, the trees and houses faster, the roadside hedges faster still'. 'Jill looks through that blue glass, I look through this red glass' really means: 'Jill's face goes blue, my universe goes red'.

What a cover-up! Words can talk me into and out of anything, into 'seeing' what isn't seen, and out of 'seeing' what is seen. I see only what words - these little marks on paper, these peculiar noises - permit! The fatal gift of language is terribly apt to take the authenticity, the very heart, out of my life. Swallowing this poison, the 1st Person is hell-bent on becoming 3rd, on suicide.

(c) *Language contaminates the 1st Person with thoughts and feelings*

Saying to myself and my two companions 'I worry', 'I think', 'I fear', 'I sympathise', 'I love', 'I'm in a state', etc., I suppose these sentences are complete and must mean something. In fact, they are truncated: this time the Subject is shorn of its object, instead of vice versa. They imply that I'm capable of experiencing worry, thoughts, fear, love, etc., right here in myself, without reference to objects which are worried about, thought about, feared, loved... So I come to believe in a central pool or cesspool of thoughts and feelings, flooding and polluting my interior clarity, a subjective morass, a congested inner world of my very own. But when I attend to this Spot and try to experience, right here, worry, thoughts, fear, love, and so on, I experience Nothing: it's only as they go out from the 1st Person here into the world of 3rd persons there, and adhere to their objects - for instance, to Jack and Jill - that they happen at all. Here, the Source of experience remains perfectly cool and lucid, uncontaminated by what comes out of it. 'I worry about Jack', 'I think of Jill', 'I have a pain in my chest', and so on, are, like all radial sentences, centrifugal, and I find no backwash to the 'I' end of them. I see myself to be free, pure awareness at the Centre, however much language, with its truncated sentences like 'I worry', 'I ache', 'I imagine', would persuade me otherwise.[2]

(d) *Language contaminates the 3rd person also*

Language, then, launches a threefold assault upon me - talking me into believing that I am, as 1st Person, superfluous, that I am a mere 3rd-person thing, that this thing is saturated with thoughts and feelings. It would be surprising if such a mass of delusion stopped here, and language allowed me to be right about others while I am so wrong about myself. In fact, it contaminates 3rd persons also. When I say 'Jill sees (thinks about/likes/is critical of...) me', I find it hard not to attribute consciousness to her as 3rd person, to that opaque, headed organism. Language points behind that coloured, moving surface to a ghostly inhabitant, a hobgoblin peeping at me out of those eyes, a tiny thinker busy in that head, weighing me up. All faces become demonic: I am surrounded by these special objects I can hardly bear to look at, for they are so haunted, so supercharged. To live in such a universe is very upsetting. Easy, natural, loving behaviour becomes impossible. Language is structured around the fiction of separate consciousnesses, one per body; separate consciousnesses mean alienation; alienation means despair. How could there be two sorts of consciousness - mine, which is delightfully boundless, free, uncluttered, inseparable from Consciousness in general; and theirs, which has unfortunately been divided into tiny bits and shut up in tiny boxes?[3]

Consciousness never was in those heads over there: they are in Consciousness. Consciousness isn't a thing, to be split up and shared out among things. It is the unique prerogative, the boundless Essence, of the 1st Person singular, present tense, and to imagine it lurking in 3rd persons as such is as common as it is absurd, and as absurd as it is distressing.

(e) *Language contaminates non-human objects*
Take the sentence 'Those trees are beautiful (healthy/useful/ interesting...)'. Here again is a segmental sentence which implies a radial one: so that the completed sentence reads 'I see (feel/think/ believe...) they are beautiful, etc.'. In practice, I find that when I ignore this radial component - when I engage in one-way looking and overlook this 1st Person - I inevitably assume myself to be a thing here relating to a thing there. Instead of containing it, I am up against it, limited by it, perhaps threatened by it. Certainly I'm not open to it; I'm unable to see it clearly, without bias, just as it's given. But when, viewing myself as No-thing filled with that thing, I become it, I see it as it is. When, beguiled by language, I think I am in the world, I am blinded by the world; but when, coming to my senses, I see the world is in me, I really see it.

36

(f) *Conclusion*

SCIENCE-3 has inherited the language of common sense, which is the language of make-believe. It is society's most effective weapon for suppressing the - always dangerous - 1st Person. One of the main practical functions of SCIENCE-1 is to see through the built-in duplicity of language as we now use it; and to re-deploy it in the interests, no longer of outworn social fictions, but of what is actually given. Instead of fitting the facts to language, language must be fitted to the facts.

Suitably deployed, what deludes is what enlightens. We have in this Section used language to expose its own double-talk and to re-habilitate 1st-Personhood. For this purpose, as we noted in Section 17, it is already well suited. In the service of SCIENCE-1 it can prove as honest as, in the service of SCIENCE-3 and common sense, it has proved corrupt.

[1]ECKHART: *The word SUM, I AM, can be spoken by no creature, but by God only.*
DEVIKALOTTARA: *I am alone. I am the Supreme Brahman... Such is the settled conviction of the Mukta. All other experience leads to bondage.*

[2]SANKARA: *Having realised his real Self as space, the Sage, without attachments and desires, clings to nothing.*

[3]PAI-YUN: *Where others dwell, I do not dwell... Where others go I do not go. This doesn't mean that I refuse to associate with other people, but that black and white must be distinguished.*
EUGEN HERRIGEL: *What you then experience with regard to your own self is not transferred by analogy to other selves, still less to things; all these other forms are directly experienced too, from the Origin.*

19: SCIENCE-1 IS NEVER BORING

It would be natural to expect that the basic discovery of SCIENCE-1, having once been made and tested, would then cease to interest. What could be duller than the vision of absolute Emptiness, unless it were that vision relentlessly repeated till it filled - or emptied - one's whole life? At least the discoveries of SCIENCE-3 offer something to get one's teeth into; at least they display some content - even if that content is often unappetising and thin and abstract, and gets rapidly less exciting as the initial thrill of discovery wears off.

One of the paradoxes of the Emptiness here is how, though forever the same, it gets more intriguing, more surprising, more wonderful, more precious, the more it is noticed. Here, and here alone, familiarity breeds respect, dedication, reverence. This isn't a matter of theory but of observation, each for himself. But the consistent report is that everything - when taken by itself - sooner or later grows dull and boring, whereas the No-thing it comes from never loses its brightness. Nor is this the end of the story. The surprisingly happy sequel is this: all these emergent things, so tiresome on their own, when seen in the only way they really can be seen, from the station of their Origin here, are bathed in the glow of that Origin; they have the refreshing taste of their Source; they smell of their native land, the Country of Everlasting Clearness. So it happens that, while SCIENCE-3 is often hard and disappointing and dreary work, SCIENCE-1 is simple and rewarding and fascinating work - and not so much work at all as enjoyment and rest.

And of course it is exceedingly appropriate that the Emptiness should thus fascinate, that it should prove the obsession to end all obsession. True, it couldn't be plainer - but what a magically resourceful Plainness it is! From this white Light the gorgeous kaleidoscope of the universe endlessly radiates, out of this infra-microscopic Top-hat are drawn all the props and all the actors that come and go on the world's stage. How beautiful that this marvellous Cornucopia should be alive to itself, and how right that its own Self-awareness in me should never pall! For *deserved* interest, for genuine worthwhileness, what in the world can compare with Where it all comes from? If this 1st Person has any complaint, surely it is that the products out there aren't boring enough, and that their dreariness is so slow to drive one back to their Primary Producer here.[1]

[1]ERIGENA: *Every visible and invisible creature is a theophany, or appearance of God.*
GAMPOPA: *It is a great joy to realise that the Fundamental Nature is qualityless.*
TE-SHAN: *Emptiness functions mysteriously, Vacuity works wonders.*

20: SCIENCE-1 IS DISINTERESTED

A t its best, SCIENCE-3 brings out the best in a man - humility in the face of the evidence, reverence for the truth however alarming or improbable, tireless patience and dedication, and detachment from results, from all gain and loss.[1] But of course SCIENCE-3 is rarely quite so disinterested, and SCIENTIST-3 never. He has his job, his reputation, his family to think of. It is SCIENCE-1 that perfects the virtues of SCIENCE-3. Indeed the very nature of its material ensures that SCIENCE-1 is wholly disinterested, with no eye on the pay-off - whether that pay-off be material or psychological or spiritual. (And notably the last; the most effective barrier to Enlightenment is religion itself, our spiritual acquisitiveness.) Nothing is to be gained from Nothing. SCIENCE-1 works only so long as attention is paid, without concepts or ulterior motives (or indeed any motives), to the absolutely plain Datum here in all its poverty and holding no promise of reward. It makes no difference that, paradoxically, this Poverty produces infinite wealth. The Absence is for acceptance as absence, not as the presence of a well-concealed gold-mine. The gold comes out all right, but unsought, in its own good time and unpredictable shape.

Unlike SCIENCE-1, SCIENCE-3 always has the problem of apportioning its limited resources between pure research and its practical applications. Truth and utility - the detached search for knowledge on one hand and the personal or social exploitation of that knowledge on the other - aren't easily reconciled, or for long. SCIENCE-1, on the other hand, has no such problem. It *is* pure science. In fact, it is the only discipline that seeks no profit - whether for the scientist himself, or his nation, or the world.

[1]WILLIAM JAMES: *When one turns to the magnificent edifice of the physical sciences, and sees how it was reared; what thousands of disinterested moral lives of men lie buried in its mere foundations; what patience and postponement, what choking down of preference, what submission to the icy laws of outer fact are wrought into its very stones and mortar; how absolutely impersonal it stands in its vast augustness, - then how besotted and contemptible seems every little sentimentalist who comes blowing his voluntary smoke-wreaths and pretending to decide things from out of his private dream!*

21: SCIENCE-1 IS FERTILE

One mark of the really important discoveries of SCIENCE-3 is that they spill over from their original field into neighbouring ones, fertilising them also. (The paradigm is the idea of Evolution, which quickly spread from botany and zoology into most other disciplines, to their great benefit.) At first sight, what SCIENCE-1 discovers - the Void - must be void of anything of value to SCIENCE-3. In fact, however, SCIENCE-3 owes an immense debt to SCIENCE-1. This debt includes one of a very specific kind. SCIENCE-3 is based on mathematics - a mathematics which is based on Zero or *Sunya*, which in turn is none other than the Void which is the goal of Eastern meditation. Islamic philosophers got it from Indian sages. And now, aren't we beginning to find here in the West, among the unsought and unexpected benefits proceeding from experience of this same mindless Void (i.e. the 1st Person), all the adventures of the mind, all the intellectual fecundity we could reasonably ask for? In particular, haven't we here the solution of those perennial problems which SCIENCE-3 and common sense are forever posing but cannot solve? In this Essay we are only beginning to explore the inspiration that can flow from conscious 1st-Personhood.

And surely it is only to be expected that, so long as I fabricate here this central obstruction, this nut of a head, this solid and opaque ball or blob, to serve as the nucleus of my universe, then I am not only hard and hard-faced, but also dense and small-minded, my vision is blocked, my understanding blurred and darkened, my world-picture distorted. With such a spanner thrown in my works, it's a wonder they work at all. And, conversely, when I dissolve this imaginary lump by seeing What's really here, then it is only to be expected that the universe ranged round this simple Clarity (or better, within it) should itself be illuminated and restored to its native order. To be wrongheaded (and to be headed here *is* to be wrong) about the central fact of my world is to be wrong about the rest. Expecting otherwise (as if one could be sane outside and mad inside) is like expecting a watch to go without its mainspring, a tree to flourish without its root, a lamp to shine without wick or oil. How odd that the one spot in the universe which I had systematically overlooked turns out to be the Spot that matters, the more-than-holy Ground which is, precisely, the Solution of all problems and the Fountain-head of all creation![1]

Nor can it be said of SCIENCE-1 that it solves old puzzles without generating any interesting new ones, that it inspires no programmes of research and discovery in the objective field of SCIENCE-3, and that at least in this sense it is barren. Quite the reverse: there now opens out an array of problems demanding investigation by ordinary scientific means. For instance, it has been noticed that while a subject is seeing into his Voidness his pulse rate is likely to be slower, his breathing shallower and slower (sometimes almost imperceptible), his muscles more relaxed, his senses more acute, his work-output raised in quantity and quality, his concentration more sustained, his communication with others easier, his shyness and other morbid symptoms reduced if not eliminated. There is some evidence, via encephalography, that the electrical impulses of the brain are much modified. In all sorts of ways that still have to be explored, clearly seeing What one is centrally makes a great difference to what one is peripherally. Certainly we can say, then, that the wonderful fertility of SCIENCE-1 extends far into SCIENCE-3.

But all this is peanuts, compared with the inspirational role of SCIENCE-1. Briefly, it works out like this: Science and its applications have two contrasting modes of progression - by a succession of small steps, and occasional leaps. That's to say: by gradual improvements of existing ideas and devices, alternating with the invention of new ones. Its thinking is mainly gradual and unsurprising or *linear,* and occasionally sudden and inspired or *lateral.* [2] The development of the sailing ship over thousands of years, from a one-masted square-rigged lugger to a four-masted barque or schooner, was the product of linear thinking. Whereas the shift from a sailing ship to a paddle steamer, to a screw-propelled ship, to a hovercraft, was in each case the product of lateral thinking. *Lateral thinking is the business of SCIENCE-1, linear thinking the business of SCIENCE-3.* And *both* are your business and mine.

For the new to come the old must go, and SCIENCE-1 is ever new, ever making a fresh start. Wide-openness without preconceptions, which plucks ideas, unforseeable and dewy-fresh, from thin air - this is the speciality, the expertise, the hallmark, the very lifeblood of SCIENCE-1. It has no laurels to rest on, no propositions to prove, no opinions to defend. In fact, no past at all, in total contrast to SCIENCE-3. They couldn't be more different here or more complementary. One supplies the inspiration, the other the perspiration, which none of us can afford to be without.

[1]TAI-HUI: *The precious Vajra sword is right here and its purpose is to cut off the head.*
RUMI: *Behead yourself!*
ATTAR: *You must choose one of two things - either have your head cut off or go into exile... He who loves Me, but loves his head better, is no true lover.*
HAFIZ: *How wonderful is the path of love, where the headless one is exalted!*

[2]I am indebted to the works of Edward De Bono for these useful terms.

22: THE TUNNEL: SCIENCE-1 ESTABLISHES MY IMMORTALITY

Nowadays, thanks to the wonders of intensive care, more and more patients who have almost died (some have actually been pronounced "clinically dead") are resuscitated to tell their story. It turns out to be a surprisingly consistent and positive story, of which the chief features are these. The patient finds himself stationed at a distance of a few feet from the stricken body, surveying it with some detachment. Next, he is propelled through a dark tunnel towards a Light shining at the far end. Joining that Light, he discovers it to be incomparably brilliant but not at all dazzling. He may find himself merging into that Light, which, so far from being merely physical, is more like a conscious and welcoming Entity. Whether this Entity is recognised as God, or Christ, or some other Divine Being, or the Light of Consciousness Itself, depends (not surprisingly) on the beliefs and expectations of the patient. Finally, on his recovery and return to daily life, he discovers that his fear of death has much diminished, or has gone altogether.

There are many minor elaborations and variations of this Near Death Experience. No two NDEs are the same. Nevertheless these three main ingredients - the distancing, the tunnel, and the Light at the end of it - are the norm to which you and I may look forward with confidence.

Yes, this large and fast-growing body of evidence about the run-up to death is heartening, to say the least. Only a determined defeatist or kill-joy, hell-bent on self-destruction, could dismiss it as of no interest whatever. Nevertheless, all such evidence is anecdotal, a matter of hear-say. Short of anticipating his own deathbed by making a serious suicide attempt, SCIENTIST-3 has no way of verifying it. And even if he could deliberately achieve his NDE and survive the ordeal, it would remain a *Near* Death Experience - and a near miss here is no better than light-years off-target. He would still have no means of knowing what an *All-the-way* Death Experience would be like: no means of checking whether this much-extolled NDE is anything more than a brief wish-fulfilling stage or last-minute let-up on the road to total extinction. After all, none of these dying patients has actually died, and come back from the far side of death to tell his tale.

Small wonder, then, that SCIENTIST-3 is reluctant to accept NDEs as evidence about his experience at the time of death itself. They hold out no certain hope of immortality. As a scientist, he cannot take them as seriously as, in his private and personal capacity, he might like to do.

This is where SCIENCE-1 comes to the rescue - by going all the way into and through death. And doing so, moreover, right now, in the thick of our life, by means of a simple experiment that can be repeated anywhere, by anyone, at any time.

In fact, I'm asking you to repeat, right now, the tunnel experiment which you were required to do in the Prologue, but this time more thoroughly.

Open out your tunnel again like this:

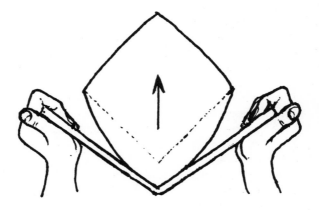

Fit your face into one end, hold the other up to your bathroom mirror, and *trust what you see in there.*

Observe, at one end, yourself as 3rd person, on display as eyes, nose, mouth, cheeks, and so on, belonging to an all-too-mortal human being. All quite normal, *nothing* missing. Now shift your attention to the other end of the tunnel, where *everything* is missing, to yourself as 1st Person on display here as Aware Emptiness, not empty Emptiness but filled Emptiness, bare Capacity for those familiar human features. Also as Capacity for every other mortal thing that happens to present itself, in and out of tunnels.

Evidently this is now *your* end of the tunnel, the near end where the seeing is, while the far end is where the seen is. And evidently here at the near end there is nothing to you, and you are in yourself deader than the deadest doornail. Right here, as 1st Person, you lack everything, including life and shape and substance and change and all the things of time. And, just because you are empty of it all, you are empty for it all. You consciously vanish in favour of whatever's on offer. Dying to your sole self and living as all the others, all life is yours, and you pass through death to eternal life.

Let me put it in less paradoxical and more down-to-earth terms. What you appear to be depends on the distance of your observer. Thus at a range of 16 inches (400 cm), over there at the far end of the tunnel, you are on display as a mortal human being: whereas at the range of 0 inches, at your end of the tunnel, you are on display as Nothing of the kind, or of any kind.

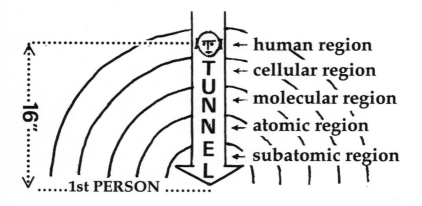

As for the intermediate stages between 16 inches and 0 inches - regions where you figure in turn as cellular, molecular, atomic, and sub-atomic, our tunnel does what tunnels are for. It bores through them all, regardless, and arrives at the No-thing that's aware of itself as beyond them all. Arrives at the Central Reality that's giving rise to those regional appearances, at the Light of Consciousness that's lighting them up, at (in short) the 1st Person Singular, Present Tense.

Other people's story of their journey, through Providence's tunnel, to join that immortal Light, *encourage* me to believe in my own immortality. But it is my story, my own journey now through this other tunnel to the very same Light, which establishes that belief on a firm empirical basis. Taken together, the two stories convince. You could describe them as complementary. In fact, our tunnel has some outstanding advantages: though constructed of paper, it is well-engineered. It is much less costly, is better lit, is quieter (the NDE tunnel is often noisy), is quite painless, and it takes one all the way through death every time, and out the other side. Above all, it enables one to make this most actual-factual and crucial of journeys - the journey Home - at will as occasion demands, at one's own pace and free from deathbed pressures and anxieties. So put in your Homework now, I say, and you won't be caught out, won't find yourself on your deathbed unprepared and unfit to enjoy to the full its matchless blessings. Go on making this journey back to the place you never really left and "you need no longer tremble over the body, seeing that you are not with it for a single hour, but are always elsewhere." - It's Rumi I'm quoting. - "Where are you and where is the body? You are in one valley, and the body is in another. This body is a great deception, a great hoodwink."

Right here, then, is the Divine Light-that-I-am which lights up over there the human face-that-I-have. But this is only one of my faces. I have others perhaps more handsome and certainly much brighter, probably far less battered, and every bit as indispensable. For example, when I stretch out a much longer, a truly telescopic arm as far as the Moon (with my lunar mirror at the

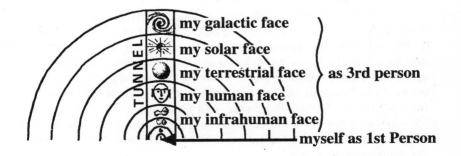

my galactic face

my solar face

my terrestrial face ⟩ as 3rd person

my human face

my infrahuman face

myself as 1st Person

TUNNEL

49

end of it instead of my bathroom mirror) what do I find in it but my Earth face - white and blue and brown and beautiful, ever-changing, long-lived, nevertheless ageing and doomed to die?

And, of course, this is neither the end of the story nor of the tunnel. Extending my telescopic arm still further, I find in its mirror my Solar face, that planet-ringed star. Very charming and bright and long-lived it is, but again not for ever. And beyond even that is my Galactic face, that spiral island universe: which is still, of course, a material thing, and in time all material things perish. Only the Timeless One, of whom these are the many faces, survives them all. As this One who is myself as 1st Person, I am the heart of the matter and all matter, the very life and soul of the cosmic party, and all its shining faces are my very own.[1]

Historical Note

Our paper tunnel came into being at a workshop held in Toronto in 1971, some years before I read, in Dr. Moody's *Life After Death* (1975), about the NDE tunnel. It began as a truncated garbage bag. Ever since then, my friends and I have been carrying paper tunnels round the world. Tens of thousands of people have been in there, have seen what dies at the far end, and seen and been - however briefly - what cannot die at the near end. And a relatively small but significant proportion of them are now consciously living, against all the odds, in and from and by that undying Light. Of our twenty-five or so devices for unveiling the Light, the paper tunnel has proved the most powerful. I'm learning to see why. A tunnel happens to be the Almighty's chosen mise-en-scène for revealing Himself at the hour of our death. In that case, what more fitting mise-en-scène than our own version of the very same device for revealing Him all the days of our life?

Certainly He doesn't despise it. That the Highest should deign to turn up, not this time in a birth tunnel and a manger, but in a tatty old Canadian garbage bag, witnesses equally to his humour and his humility, to his lovingkindness and his mercy. Heaven's power and glory are *that* kind of power, *that* kind of glory! Any two consecutive pages in any of the millions of books on theology and metaphysics in the British Library, sellotaped together to form a minitunnel, have more to tell me about Him, and myself, and the nature of Reality, and what Life and Death really are, than all those volumes lumped together.

[1]PLOTINUS: *Clear away (what is foreign), then look. Or rather, let a man first purify himself, then observe: he will not doubt his immortality when he sees himself thus entered into the Pure, the Intellectual.*

To what degree is disengagement from the body possible? Disengagement simply means that the soul withdraws to its own place.

BUDDHA: *You cannot by going reach that place wherein there are no birth, no ageing, no decaying, no falling away, no rising up again in rebirth. You cannot by going come to such a place.*

DOGEN: *The sage leaves life and death to the mind, he leaves them to the body.*

RABBI BUNUM OF PZHYSHA: *Everyone must have two pockets, so that he can reach into one or the other according to his needs. In his right pocket are to be the words "For my sake the world was created", and in his left, "I am dust and ashes".* (In our terms, the right pocket is the Light at one end of the tunnel, and the left pocket is what it shines on at the other end.)

23: SCIENCE-1 PUTS ME IN TOUCH WITH
THE EXTERNAL WORLD

Truly SCIENCE-3 needs SCIENCE-1: it gets into muddles which only SCIENCE-1 can clear up. An outstanding instance is the problem of my knowledge of the outside world. How, according to SCIENCE-3, am I now able to see these words, to hear the rustle of the paper as I turn the page, to feel its smoothness and the warmth of the room, to smell these flowers, to taste this cup of tea? Reduced to essentials, the official answer is that the surface of my body is provided with specialised receptors sensitive to a variety of incoming wave-motions and other stimuli; and these receptors (some localised in eyes and ears and nose and tongue, others distributed over my skin) translate the external stimuli into code-messages which are then transmitted by nerve fibres to a certain region of my brain; and it's not till these converging messages arrive here at their terminus that I experience anything of the external world. Actually, therefore, all I know about is a brain-condition, the behaviour of a collection of particles in my head. The rest is inference, a long shot in the dark.

As it stands, this story is nonsense. Firstly it does the opposite of what it sets out to do, and explains how I *can't* know anything about the external world! All the chances are that what it's like outside my head - supposing there *is* a head or an outside - is vastly different from what I find inside; and, anyway, there's no means of telling. These words and this page and this hand, the face I see in my mirror, the friends around me - the world itself - are, for all I can tell to the contrary, a private dream. Secondly, the whole story told by SCIENTIST-3 - his tale of light-waves arriving from the Sun and sound-waves travelling in Earth's atmosphere, of eyes and ears, nerve fibres, brain, and all the rest - is itself part of the dream and no more valid than any other part; for he can hardly abolish the world I perceive while leaving intact those portions which (he claims) enable me to perceive it! Thirdly, his story isn't merely self-invalidating but incredible. I just can't believe that this brilliant white paper and this agile hand, these Spring flowers and their delightful scent, this tea and the subtle taste of it, are goings-on in something like a meat-ball or a can of corned beef; and that my cat, who seems to be sitting in the sunlight over there, is really sitting in my head here. Fourthly, his story doesn't even try to explain how my vast world could shut itself up in a tiny part of itself without shrinking the one or distending the other - a compression more improbable and a trick more magical than imprisoning a six-foot man in his toe-nail, a mansion in one of its bricks, or the length and breadth of England in Nelson's Column - without doing the slightest injury to either party. On all counts, then, this story of SCIENCE-3 is too absurd to pass even as science-fiction, and certainly too fantastic for any scientist to bother with except in the course of his profes-sional work. Compared with this modern myth, those of primi-tive men are eminently rational. And yet - to complete my aston-ishment - SCIENCE-3 insists that it's true, and substantiated all day and every day in operating theatres and laboratories and everywhere else!

SCIENCE-1 tells an utterly different tale, one which is not only self-consistent and convincing, but also makes sense of the story of SCIENCE-3; and this it does, as always, by removing the confusion between 1st Person and 3rd. Its tale - which is my own tale, the moment-to-moment discovery of this 1st Person singular - is that there is no eye here to see things with, no ear to hear sounds with, no nose and tongue here to smell and taste with, no brain here to receive messages or to think with. At this instant there is Nothing *this* side of these words, of this paper, of these hands, of those flowers, of that cat; Nothing in their way; Nothing here to register or process or pass information concerning them; no seer or seeing but only these moving coloured shapes; no hearer or hearing but only these sounds; no smeller, taster, feeler, experiencer, thinker, but only these odours and tastes and textures, and these thoughts about them. All is immediately given, simply present; it is just how it is, where it is, un-interfered with. Or - to put the matter another way - only in the *Absence* of eyes, ears, nose, tongue, brain, do the seen and heard and smelled and tasted occur, and even a particle or a shadow of a receiving agency here would be enough to blot them out. What is called sense-experience happens, not in and to a finite body, a local thing, but in and to this infinite Emptiness which is myself-at-large, myself as I am to myself.[1] This is the way the universe comes - all duly set out in this 1st Person. I don't live in the world, it lives in me; and it doesn't live in any head-cage, but out-of-doors - free, shining, energetic, parading its colours, noisily showing off and disporting itself in this immense playground I provide it with. Indeed, now the imagined centre has dropped out of my life, I am both playground and everyone in it, the whole world just as it appears. How, then, could I have any problem of getting in touch with it? For the 1st Person there is no *external* world.

The 3rd person, on the other hand, lives in the world, is a tiny thing surrounded by and fortified against a huge thing, and consequently there arises the all-important problem of communication between them. SCIENCE-3, investigating this problem, pieces together its story of stimuli arriving from the outside world - all of which applies perfectly to the 3rd person. For it isn't an account of how he *experiences* the world (as 3rd person, he doesn't) but of how he *connects with* the world, a tale of scrutable things, of objects or phenomena, of chains of incoming and outgoing physical causation which are nowhere interrupted by any such inscrutable irrelevancy as 'knowledge of the external world'. Thus rectified, the story of SCIENCE-3 is as consistent in theory as it is indispensable in practice. *False as a description of how this 1st Person is conscious of the outside world, it is true as a description of how that 3rd person is modified by and adjusts to the outside world.*

Once more, then, SCIENCE-1 corrects SCIENCE-3 by going one step further, pushing it beyond itself to its inevitable conclusion. SCIENCE-3 tries to reduce my vast world to something in my head, while SCIENCE-1 goes on to reduce my head to Nothing - a Nothing which explodes into Vastness. And this Vastness is inhabited by myriads of 3rd persons whose heads are all just heads, in no danger of having the world stuffed into them, and therefore proper objects for SCIENCE-3 to study.

[1]*BRIHADARANYAKA UPANISHAD: There is no seer but Him, no-one to hear but Him, no-one thinking, no-one aware but Him.*
BANKEI: *It is the Unborn which sees and hears.*
AL-ARABI: *Only God has seeing, hearing.*
LIEH-TZU: *I look and listen without using eyes and ears.*

24: SCIENCE-1 IS ULTRA-SCEPTICAL

SCIENCE-3 is a great exorcist and debunker, the implacable enemy of superstition and the irrational fears that go with it. All its progress has been won, in the teeth of fierce resentment, at the expense of those unfounded beliefs which were simply the common sense of their day and not so much hallowed as obvious. It has been the work of many centuries to adjure, for example, such mystic entities as Star-moving gods and Nature-supervising angels, a Cosmocrat and his Laws of Nature, Gravity and Levity, Phlogiston, Animal Spirits, the Life Force, etc., with the result that the universe of SCIENCE-3 is now comparatively unhaunted.

Comparatively so - for SCIENCE-3 is by no means a consistent cosmic exorcist. It is true that, insofar as SCIENCE-3 is strictly scientific, it takes no account of such ghostly entities as Life and Mind and Consciousness, but its less exact branches cannot easily ignore them. And in any case there remains the underlying assumption, the creed which goes unquestioned: "I believe in other minds, or in a plurality of spirits, or in consciousnesses'. Whatever his professional attitude, the private opinion of SCIENTIST-3 is that each human shape he confronts has, lurking in the upper part of it, a spook (or elf or sprite or fairy or spectre of some sort) which is peeping out at him through those two little windows in a more-or-less threatening manner. Even though the world is now for him de-populated of free-ranging spirits and godlings, these imprisoned ones remain, and they are charged with all the old threat and promise - but specially threat. Indeed they render their shrines - which are people's heads - so possessed, so supernatural and privileged and disturbing, that these hairy spheres (curiously punctured and rubberised) constitute a very special class of thing, not treated at all like ordinary lumps of matter. SCIENTIST-3 may well deny entertaining any such superstition, but his behaviour in the presence of these peculiar objects - ranging from slight disturbance to acute embarrassment - gives him away. In particular, he may find quite unbearable the steady, clear gaze of the young child and of the childlike seer.

SCIENCE-3 fights the war against superstition; SCIENCE-1 wins it. It does so by exorcising *every* remaining sprite and ghost from the objective universe, and particularly those last-ditch ones which haunt human heads and the heads of some of the higher animals. For SCIENTIST-1, when confronted by the face at the far end of the tunnel, or any other face, sees the total asymmetry of the set-up, and takes seriously what he sees. At this near end is matter-free Emptiness (call it Mind or Consciousness or Spirit or what you like) and at that far end its filling of coloured and moving shapes (call it matter or body or thing or what you like). Anyhow, the Emptiness here is speckless, simple, indivisible, not-two, boundless; and its filling there just the opposite in all respects. Both sides are to be taken exactly as given - all the 'mind' in the world here and all the 'matter' there, without any horse-trading or compromise. This doesn't mean that I deny your Emptiness (or Consciousness) but that I find it only here, *my* side of your face, as my own Emptiness and that of all other beings. For there is indeed plenty of it here - more than enough for everybody - and it isn't any kind of object or thing, and least of all the kind of thing that could be cut up and parcelled out and handed round to separate lumps of matter. So I see that *your face is no more than your appearance and I am no less than your Reality.* If I call this Reality my Original Face, I must add that it is yours too, and everyone's.[1]

And truly it is one of the unforeseen pleasures of the 1st-Person life to gaze unabashed into the faces of one's friends, without feeling or thinking anything in particular, and just see them for what they always were - *things for looking at and never for looking out of.* This isn't an unloving stare, reducing you to a cardboard cut-out. Quite the reverse; it is a most loving refusal to separate my Consciousness from yours, and it removes the last barrier between us. Liberated from the superstition of plural spirits, we are at last really one. This is the perfect love which casts out fear - the fear inseparable from living in a haunted world.

Thus SCIENTIST-1 presents SCIENTIST-3 with his royal charter, his right to take up quite unashamedly his behaviouristic and materialistic stance and cease having a bad conscience about, or cease trying to find some home for, those hobgoblins called other people's minds. *The science of the object can afford to drop the superstition of even a twinge of consciousness there, because the science of the Subject (with equal scepticism) has dropped the superstition of even a speck of matter here.*

This isn't quite the end of the story. The final de-bunking to the credit of SCIENCE-1 is the exorcism of that residual entity, that toughest and most persistent and most specious of all ghosts - Consciousness itself, as one huge Spirit absorbing hosts of tiny sprites, as a single Higher Self made up of all individual selves, as a Someone or Something having any kind of objective reality. Here, words are unavailing: all they can do is objectify the subject - which is impossible. The best course to take is to cease verbalising and look again here (at the near end of the tunnel), notice that the really Real isn't real at all in the sense that objects are real, and keep silence.

[1]ZAZEN-GI: *Loosing and dropping off body and mind, your Original Face is clear before you.*
DAITO-KOKUSHI: *Not one of the seventeen hundred koans of Zen has any other purpose than to make us see our Original Face.*
RUMI: *He that beholds his own Face - his light is greater than the light of the creatures. Though he die, his sight is everlasting, because his sight is the sight of the Creator.*
THE KORAN: *Everything perishes but His Face.*

25: SCIENCE-1 GIVES THE UNIVERSE MEANING

Insofar as SCIENCE-3 is true to itself and rigorously objective, dismissing as vague or mystical or mythical all subjectivity, it confronts a meaningless world, a 'fortuitous concourse of atoms', a closed universe in which all events hang together in mutual dependence, and in which are found no gaps where 'mind' or 'consciousness' or 'purpose' could insinuate themselves - much less influence the relentless train of merely physical occurrences. In this universe, life is a rare and brief and insignificant accident, and mind (if it is recognised at all) a mere by-product of blind forces, a sort of occasional phosphorescence, an epiphenomenon. In principle, all is accounted for without the hypothesis of consciousness.

As we have just seen, this is precisely the sort of universe which SCIENTIST-3 might be expected to discover; it fits him. All the same, this isn't a pleasant world to be thrown into, and most scientists (unless they are exceptionally honest, or exceptionally pessimistic, or both) join the layman in ignoring it; or at least they shed it daily with their white coats and take off-duty comfort in the closer and warmer human scene. SCIENCE-3 is for taking seriously, but not *that* seriously! Nevertheless a man's basic assumptions matter, and below the surface grow the fear and the despair that come from living in a universe which is quite indifferent, if not actively hostile, to all he holds dear. The occupational disease of SCIENTIST-3 is universitis: he suffers from a deficiency in his cosmos.

SCIENCE-1 makes good the deficiency. The universe I find myself in is meaningful throughout because, in fact, I find it in me, and I am its meaning. This universe occurs to and in and from the Void which I am here and which unites me with all things whatsoever.[1] Accordingly for me as 1st Person there exist no mere 3rd persons, no intrinsically opaque bodies, no objects that aren't Void-based, and therefore none that is not myself; thus the world contains not so much as an atom that is alien to me, nothing that need frighten me, and indeed no creature that I can spare and wash my hands of. This isn't wishful thinking but honest seeing: it is the scientific realism which refuses to go on pretending that observation needs no Observer, object no Subject, 3rd person no 1st Person, and which refuses to go on pretending that the scientist has somehow taken leave of the universe and is surveying it from some mysterious limbo of his own.

But *of course* my universe is mindless and meaningless, so long as I overlook that standing proof to the contrary - myself as 1st Person! *Of course* it is dead, so long as I insist on amputating myself from its body and bleeding the thing to death! *Of course* its play of particles is purely accidental, so long as I make an exception of that sample packet which is here so purposefully denying purpose! *Of course* Nature's secret is hidden from me, so long as I treat myself as supernatural (or rather, unnatural) and dare not look into her at that one Spot where she lies wide open to inspection - *this* side of my spectacles and *this* end of my telescope or microscope! If I live in a clockwork universe it is because I am playing SCIENTIST-3 instead of being SCIENTIST-1, and wilfully ignoring its most obvious and least clockworklike feature. None is so wretchedly blind as the man who's determined to keep his eyes shut.

[1]CHUANG-TZU: *He who clearly sees that, while treating things as things, he is no thing himself - how could he be content to govern the hundred clans of the world? ... He is the Sole Possessor.*
BLAKE: *More, More! is the cry of a mistaken soul; less than All cannot satisfy man.*
D. T. SUZUKI: *Zen masters are totally identified with Nature.*

26: SCIENCE-1 IS WORLD-ASSERTING

On the face of it, SCIENCE-3 regards the universe with the utmost veneration, while SCIENCE-1 is world-despising and world-denying - or even world-destroying, since (seemingly) it dismisses all things as phantasms, mere apparitions of the one Reality which is No-thing. On further scrutiny, however, the truth is the other way round. Certainly SCIENCE-3 began as one would expect - progressively purging Nature of magical notions, humbling itself before the facts as given out there in all their intractable aseity and concreteness, and as in no sense the scientist's own creation. And certainly SCIENCE-3 has never officially repudiated this respectful attitude to Nature's richness. Nevertheless its built-in contradiction-system ensures that here again the more it succeeds the more it fails. The progress of SCIENCE-3 is the regress of its universe, its systematic impoverishment. All the qualities of things - not only their beauty and ugliness, their lovableness and hatefulness, their life and mind, but also their sound and smell and taste and feel, their colour and shape, their hardness and softness - all these have been stealthily transported, piecemeal over the centuries, from the perceived object over there to the perceiving subject here. They have become subjective instead of objective, the observer's private reaction instead of his public discovery, his personal contribution to the datum, which datum gets more and more shadowy till it practically vanishes. In the end, nothing is left in the universe of SCIENCE-3 but the bare substratum with its inane play of unscrutable energies; all the rest - the universe as actually experienced - having been drawn into the head of the experiencer. This is world-denial with a vengeance! And what could be more wildly supernatural - or more superstitious - than this immense, brilliant, colourful, noisy, boisterous, ungovernable world done up in a neat parcel and posted in an eight-inch bone letter-box - leaving the world outside the letter-box a lifeless desert?

Of course, such an in-gathering of qualities was inevitable. There's nothing wrong with this inflation of the observer at the expense of the observed, this impossible feat of head-packing, *provided the head is now examined from inside and seen as the head of the 1st Person.* Then it is found to be, after all, as roomy as the world: indeed it *is* the world![1] And this world is seen still to be decorated with all those qualities and values that had apparently been stripped from it. All is as it was; all the colours and shapes and sounds, the meaning and the beauty, the life and the mind, remain at their ancient stations and the universe is itself again. In other words, SCIENTIST-1 is at large, world-wide, unbounded, insepara-ble from the Cosmos itself. Thus his ideas about the stars are indeed about the stars up there and not about his head here; they are sidereal, not cranial. Thus the colour and scent and feel of a flower, and all his thoughts and feelings about the flower, belong out there to the flower and aren't torn from it and injected by some magic syringe into his cranium. He feels the flower and not his finger-tips, smells the flower and not his nose - and certainly not his brain. All things are just as they appear in their native glory, and only he, the 1st Person, is lacking - absolutely. In fact, he has no mind *of his own* at all, no personal or central experience or life or substance or manhood or thinghood or quality of any sort, but only Emptiness, this boundless Empty-headedness - which is filled with all creation. What he misses in himself he gets back, with immense interest added, in others. Seeing himself as Nothing, he is all set to enjoy Everything.

[1]H. H. PRICE: *If the sense-data are literally inside the brain we are committed to the conclusion that they are always smaller than the things to which they belong, or else that our head is very much larger than it appears to be from touch.*
HUANG-PO: *This travelling hat may look small, but when I put it on it covers the whole cosmos.*
RUMI: *How can a world be contained in the clay of the body?*

27: SCIENCE-1 NORMALISES 'PARANORMAL' PHENOMENA

The close-knit fabric of SCIENCE-3 is marvellously patterned, but it has frayed edges and numerous ragged holes which refuse to be patched. These include such intractable areas as telepathy, clairvoyance, clairaudience, precognition, recollection of past lives, automatic writing, psychometry, hauntings, possession, mediumship. If the basic assumptions of SCIENCE-3 are altogether valid, things of this sort should not happen. But they do happen, giving notice that there is a radical mistake somewhere. Something essential has been left out, it seems. Anyway, SCIENCE-3 evidently is unfitted to take account of a large class of facts, and is to that extent unscientific. The role of SCIENCE-1 is to show them in a new light - the light of the 1st Person - a light which illuminates and domesticates these so-called 'paranormal' phenomena.

As we have already noticed (Section 23), SCIENCE-3 itself proves, in its carefully circumstantial account of how a 3rd person 'experiences the world', that he could never, as 3rd person, do anything of the sort. He's too solid, and much too small. Manifestly it is I, the 1st Person, who alone am empty enough and big enough for the job. *What* I experience depends upon many things - upon the state of my physical and chemical layers, my brain, my body, my world, and ultimately upon the whole of things. *That* I experience depends upon No-thing. Awareness is the function of - it *is* - this unbounded Emptiness at the heart of my many-layered world. If I foolishly imagine that a sense-organ or a brain doesn't only *condition* what I perceive, but itself perceives; if (contrary to all present evidence) I suppose that my eyes are now busy reading and my ears hearing and my tongue tasting and my brains thinking - why of course I can't imagine how I could ever see or hear or taste or think without benefit of sensory apparatus; and either I deny that 'extra-sensory perception' occurs at all, or else I write it off as 'occult' or separate it off as 'paranormal'. But if, more reasonably, taking my own case as a true sample and my only source of inside information, I recognise that *things* don't experience anything, that eyes don't see and ears don't hear and tongues don't taste and brains don't think, that (in this sense) *all* seeing is eyeless, and so on - why then the special problem of 'extra-sensory perception', and of the 'paranormal' in general, doesn't arise.[1]

But the superstition that certain things are animated dies hard. The assumption of our primitive ancestors and our own common sense - inherited uncritically by SCIENCE-3 and rarely repudiated even now - is that consciousness is a subtle quasi-physical substance or emanation or energy which belongs in and hovers around certain very special parcels of matter, for example brains. It follows from this age-old superstition that there are as many 1st Persons as 3rd, as many consciousnesses as there are 'seats of consciousness', and that each occupies a limited region of space and time - as if it were a kind of magical gas. The extent of this spatio-temporal field, its shape, the nature of its boundaries (whether clear-cut or fuzzy), its arising and growth and decay - all such awkward questions are conveniently ignored. Merely to ask them is surely to expose the fallacy that produces them.

SCIENTIST-1, attentive to what lies at the *near* end of his telescope or microscope or viewfinder or paper bag or tunnel, no less than at the *far* end, is in a position to settle these questions. Here is nothing whatever, a Capacity so ample and unselective that it rejects nothing, an Emptiness so void that it could never be distinguished from any other emptiness, a Boundlessness so vast that it holds no hint of spatial or temporal limitation, a Plainness so simple that it is innocent of number and quality and function, a Sameness that is forever the same - and keenly aware, nevertheless, of all this. Such are the present findings of this 1st Person singular.

What calls for explanation, then, isn't why 'your mind' and 'my mind' should sometimes overlap and mingle and even change places, but why they should ever seem to be separate at all. The puzzle is the many, not the One. No wonder we are in telepathic communication if, as 1st-Person, we are that One; the surprise is that we can shut out so many of each other's thoughts and feelings. No wonder I may enter into the experience of someone else far removed in time and space if, in reality, there is no someone else, and all time and space are in me. No wonder those bundles of experience called 'souls' or 'spirits' should hang around indefinitely if, as a matter of fact, all are one indestructible Spirit.

The universe, all that is, belongs to the 1st Person.[2] Literally as well as figuratively, the totality is in the bag - at that end the manifest, at this end the rest, unmanifest. Thus all things are sorted into two classes - the actual few there, on display as the ever-changing world of the 1st Person; the potential many here, hidden in the never-changing Void of the 1st Person. Everything is polarised and accounted for: either it's what is being experienced, or what is experiencing. Nothing is lost or mislaid. The 1st Person is the magician who keeps all the tricks up his sleeve, and is continually bringing out old and new ones, and putting them back for other occasions. And all his tricks, from remembering what one had for breakfast to adventures in other worlds, are perfectly miraculous and paranormal - and perfectly natural and normal.

Potentially and in principle, accordingly, all experience throughout space and time - non-human no less than human - is accessible to this 1st Person here and now. Actually and in practice, however, only those selections from it which are more-or-less relevant to the business in hand, are presented. Otherwise, appropriate action would be impossible; one would be totally inhibited, overwhelmed with useless information and distractions.

In fact, the danger is real. If I happen to be 'psychic' or 'sensitive' I am all-too-apt to find myself flooded with the ideas and moods, the pains and illnesses, the endless problems, of others - just as if there really were others, me over against them, separate consciousnesses which, alas, aren't nearly separate enough! The upshot may well be that my unusual gifts do more harm than good, no matter how kindly my conscious intentions. And particularly so because this me-and-you attitude (face-to-face, consciousness-to-consciousness) is by nature a self-regarding and self-seeking one. The real trouble isn't that I'm too open to invasion, but not open enough. My immunity against the occupational diseases of psychic research and psychic practices is for me to see that, as 1st Person, I am totally vulnerable out there where I am forever being destroyed, and totally invulnerable here where there is nothing to destroy. I can't afford to go on overlooking this 1st Person. My safety, perhaps my sanity, my peace of mind, and my effectiveness in the exercise of these special gifts, are assured only by two-way looking. I am enabled to help people in need, without attachment, without getting swamped, without counting on specific results or any results, and without power-seeking, only when I *am* those people, because I am in myself Nothing at all.

Thus SCIENCE-1 not only takes account of and normal-
ises the 'paranormal', but guards against the dangers that go
with its study and cultivation.

[1]RUMI: *Thou seest those eyes looking, but they are like pictures on a bath-*
house wall: they do not see.
HUI-HAI: *By what means do this body or mind perceive? Can they*
perceive with the eyes, ears? ... No. Your own nature, being essentially
pure and utterly still, is capable of this perception.
ECKHART: *We cannot see the visible except with the invisible.*

[2]RILKE: *O, the world's soul will never be united*
              with mine, till what appears outside me,
              as though it always meant to be inside me,
              delightedly alights in me.

28: SCIENCE-1 FINDS THE NATURAL WORLD

Common sense has invented, and SCIENCE-3 (which is common sense systematised) has inherited and developed, a remarkable universe, having four notable peculiarities: (i) Lacking a Centre about which to organise itself, this universe is comparatively unstructured and uniform, a cosmic potato rather than a cosmic onion. (ii) Its space has three dimension of equal status, so that (for instance) a 1 inch cube is simultaneously 1 inch high x 1 inch wide x 1 inch deep; its depth is given just as its height and width are give, and in no time at all it is six-sided. (iii) In this three-dimensional space people and things stay more-or-less constant, and variations in the shape of the 1 inch cube (for instance) or in the size of a man are explained away as variations in the distance and orientation of the observer: so there's no such thing as a two-sided cube or a man the size of a pin-head. (iv) The observer himself is an accidental interloper in this universe, which is what it is and goes its own way regardless of him - of his attention, his seeing and ceasing to see, his life and death. For all the difference it makes, he might as well not be there.

Now this artificial universe is a useful aid to living in the real universe: without it, SCIENCE-3 and all its benefits, and the practical fictions we live by (and swear by), would never have got started. Civilisation itself owes everything - one might almost say civilisation *is* - this most basic of human inventions. All the same, this thought-up world, this design for a universe, this Diagram, is habitable only by diagrams, not real people. It is a science-fiction dream from which to wake up. It is a world fit only for 3rd persons and other abstractions, and in truth no world at all but a code, a set of conventions, a cosmic labour-saving device, a map for getting round the real world with.

It is when I mistake the map for the countryside that I am in real trouble. My trouble, my dishonesty, my delusion don't consist in my recognition of the artificial cosmos of SCIENCE-3 but in my conviction that it actually exists. Pretending to live in this shadowy, unnatural, unreal world, I am in danger of becoming that way myself. My remedy is the assiduous practice of SCIENCE-1, which includes the discovery of the natural world, of Nature as she actually gives herself to me - not de-natured and twisted and stretched and cut about to suit society's convenience, but Nature as she comes. Nature revealed, some would say, as the Lotus Paradise.[1]

This isn't as difficult as it sounds. No-one ever woke up one fine morning to find himself in the potato-universe of SCIENCE-3, a universe he was not the Centre of. No-one ever *saw* a world whose men and cars and houses were either present and full-size, or else absent and no-size (with no intermediate sizes at all), a world whose stars were gigantic suns, a world whose Sun was a fixture in the sky and immensely bigger than the Moon and immensely hot, a world whose Earth was a spinning ball infested with myriads of little men clinging on precariously with their boot-soles, and each of them with the universe encapsulated in his little head - not to mention the sprite that lives there too. The irony is that no-one inside or outside a mental hospital ever *really* believed in such a potato-universe, or even (if the truth were told) in an onion-universe that has for its core a solid 8 inch lump crowned with hair, instead of the *absence* of any such thing. To live in the natural world, in UNIVERSE-1, I need only have the courage of my convictions; it is enough to see what I believe and believe what I see - that this 1st Person is the empty Centre and the filled Container of the whole world. The simple truth lies wide open, and in my heart I never doubted it. What is really incredible is UNIVERSE-3, the unnatural world, the science-fiction world of SCIENCE-3, the merely 'physical' cosmos which cannot even be imagined clearly, let alone perceived.

[1]*THEOLOGIA GERMANICA: What is Paradise? All things that are.*
HAKUIN: *This very spot is the Lotus Paradise.*
TRAHERNE: *We should be as very strangers to the thoughts, customs, and opinions of men in the world, as if we were but little children.*

29: ENDLESS DISCOVERIES AWAIT SCIENCE-1

SCIENCE-1 has hardly begun to mark out, let alone explore, its own immense field, where no special skills or apparatus are needed, but only humility before the facts. The questions it asks are direct and simple. What is it really like to be me, at this moment? How is the world actually presenting itself? Exactly what control am I now exercising over it? Forgetting what I'm told and imagine, what society with its common sense and SCIENCE-3 tell me to believe, and at last daring to look for myself and to take seriously what I find - well, what do I find? I find surprise upon surprise, beyond my wildest dreams. *I see that what I had believed to be true of me and of the world is a pack of lies!*

Take just a few instances out of the unlimited range available. I notice that I annihilate and re-create the world, while *people* merely close and open their eyes.[1] I hush the world; they stop their ears. I spin the world; they pirouette.[2] I transmute the world, turning legs into grass, into trees, into hills, into sky; *people* bend down and straighten up. I go up to the stars and toss the constellations around; *people* turn their faces to the night-sky.[3] The toy chair, the wedge-shaped road, the dolls' houses, the mole-hole road tunnels - all swell to accommodate me, and shrink to nothing when I have no further use for them; *people* are obliged to shrink and swell to fit their surroundings. At will, I can turn one orange into three and back again, see through a spoon, invert a cup without spilling the tea, squash a plate without touching or breaking it, get clean through a keyhole, transpose mountains, turn a house round. I can confer upon anyone or anything the supreme honour of being the focal point, the end-product and meaning, of the universe - and demote him or it again, instantly.

Such are the powers of the 1st Person singular, the royal prerogatives of the shy King - the King who doesn't wish to know he is a king. His kingdom, the 1st-Person universe, surpasses everything he had imagined.

No distance separates him from his subjects. They appear before him in all sizes, growing and shrinking at the royal command. Their qualities and behaviour match their elasticity: thus very tiny children are quiet and intangible; and very tiny cars and tigers are slow-moving and not dangerous, though they have an alarming way of growing up fast; and stars are never large or hot or particularly far apart; and the Sun is a bright disc, smaller than a penny, sliding daily across the sky, above a vast and flat and un-moving Earth.

And so on. Such is the given world. I have still to discover another world, let alone take up residence in it. Never have I found myself in a universe of which this 1st Person was not the unchallenged monarch. Seeing this, I come to my senses, I am myself again, awake. This is going right back to where the sum went wrong, and reckoning again from there. It is returning to the innocent eye and the uncorrupted world of the new-born child and his prehuman ancestors - with a difference.[4] The child-ish overlooking of one's presence has become the childlike seeing of one's Absence; one-way looking has become two-way. This is the end of magic, of superstition, of primitive and childish fears; and of grown-up, civilised superstitions and fears also.

How odd that the only *habitable* world should be forbidden territory to the rational adult; and that, when tentatively explored by the odd Columbus or Livingstone, should appear so outlandish, so fantastic and disorderly! In fact, it isn't chaotic: everything goes on in it according to its own truly natural laws - laws which non-rational creatures don't find at all confusing. These laws are due to be codified into a new physical science - quite unlike those of SCIENCE-3 - based on phenomena as they arrange themselves, not as man re-arranges them.

Nor is this offshoot of SCIENCE-1 an optional extra, just a beautiful poem, a thrilling game, immense fun - though it's certainly these. If 'science' means 'finding out how things are', and if 'how things are' includes 'how they are given', then to ignore 'how they are given' is unscientific, and no more excus-able than any other superstition. Curiosity, intellectual integrity, ordinary honesty, are at stake - not to mention the psychological consequences of suppressing the facts and living in a world of make-believe.

The 1st Person has good reason for attending to 'how things are given'. Who is this 1st Person? From whom do these things come and to whom are they given? When the

King loses interest in the state of the kingdom and how it is being governed, he drops off again, and resumes his dream that he is one of his own subjects.

[1]RUMI: *When you shut your eyes to the world, it is abolished.*

[2]RUMI: *The Qutb (Pole) is he around whom the heavens revolve.*

[3]BLAKE: *Distance is nothing but a fantasy.*

[4]HUANG-PO: *Observe things as they are and don't pay attention to other people.*

30: SCIENCE-1 IS THE HIGHEST RELIGION

SCIENCE-3 owes much to religion; indeed one of its motives, historically, was to discover the mind of the Creator as expressed in Nature, his handiwork.[1] Increasingly, however, SCIENCE-3 has become, in effect if not in intention, anti-religious and anti-spiritual. How could it fail to become so, seeing that its settled policy, in fact its job, is to leave the Subject - the I, the Spirit - out of the picture? Of course some of its best practitioners have been religious men, but this was possible only where their science and their religion were of the sort that could be kept in idea-tight compartments; otherwise, one or the other would have exploded. The price of faith is here some lack of integrity, some double-thinking, some inner conflict. SCIENTIST-3, as such, isn't a whole man: he is spiritually handicapped. Traditional religion has some good reasons for suspecting science and obstructing its progress.

SCIENCE-1, on the other hand, is all along so profoundly religious or spiritual that it could equally well be called the religion or spirituality of the 1st Person. Note, however, that the science of the 1st Person isn't religious because it is *less* scientific than SCIENCE-3 or refuses to push doubt too far, but because it is *more* scientific, *more* inquisitive, *more* uncompromising, *more* sceptical and takes nothing at all on faith. Conversely, note that the religion of the 1st Person isn't scientific because it is *less* religious than the ordinary sort, or less dedicated to the spiritual, but because it is much more so - because it is none other than the highest. This is more than saying that SCIENCE-1 is an essentially religious enterprise; rather it is spiritual religion itself, the heart of the matter. Not that SCIENCE-1 can spare SCIENCE-3; on the contrary, SCIENCE-3 does indispensable work preparing the ground, uprooting over the centuries the outdated cosmogonies and cosmologies of religion, its tangled undergrowth of pre-scientific myths and dogmas and assumptions. But it fails to plant anything in their place. There remains only a wistful backwards look at the age of faith and cosmic meaning, only nostalgia and an aching void. SCIENCE-1 takes the ache out of that void and leaves just the Void, which is the fountain-head of all spiritual religion.

[1]EDWARD YOUNG: *The course of Nature is the art of God.*
ALEXANDER POPE: *All are but parts of one stupendous whole,*
Whose body Nature is, and God the Soul.

31: SCIENCE-1 RESTORES THE SENSE OF MYSTERY

SCIENCE-3 is at war with mystery. Inevitably, the more man knows the less it astounds him. The rainbow is an optical illusion, thunder and lightning a discharge of static electricity, Mother Earth a clod, her children a planetary scum. For he doesn't spare himself, but refers *Homo sapiens* back and back to the ever simpler life-forms from which he emerged. And even if Evolution doesn't altogether explain him away, at least it makes him appear quite ordinary and inevitable. He is no longer flabbergasted at anything, not even himself. This is a great blindness and a great loss.[1]

The morning wonder of the world can be recaptured, and perfected, only by turning away from the world to the Beholder of it. One might have thought that SCIENCE-3, with its genius for discovering new marvels in the universe, would enhance our admiration for it; and conversely that SCIENCE-1, with its genius for discovering only Emptiness, would kill our admiration outright. Not so. I find that it is when my attention is centred primarily upon the One who is attending here, and only incidentally upon the world that confronts me, that the world is made marvellous in me. Then the great surprise, the most astounding fact of all, isn't *what* the Cosmos is but *that* it is; not the infinitely varied products there but their simple Origin here.[2] Nevertheless when they are seen as proceeding from This they take on its wonder, and nothing is ordinary any more.

It is true that, in principle, SCIENCE-3 refers phenomena downwards from the macroscopic to the microscopic, and from the microscopic to the ultimate physical Substratum which is also the ultimate mystery. But it can never quite get there: the Substratum (which is the Void) isn't gained, and the mystery is lost. Only SCIENTIST-1, by turning round his attention 180° (using, for example, that perfect 'ultra-electron microscope' - the paper tunnel) can complete the story, and actually see phenomena as grounded in the Void, and therefore in Mystery itself. And what, at root, is this Science of the 1st Person but the Mystery's enjoyment of itself as infinitely incomprehensible, its perfect knowledge of itself as perfectly unknowable? 'Against all the odds', it cries, 'I actually am! Without help or spectator I have achieved the unbelievable, the impossible. Alone I'm causing *Myself*, making Myself happen. There ought to be nothing whatever. There is no reason for my Being. Yet here I am! After this, nothing is impossible, all I do is child's play, and a billion universes are chicken-feed!'. To experience this isn't to echo the Divine Astonishment, but to engage and delight in the real thing. It is incomparable.[3]

[1]PASCAL: *It is an extraordinary blindness to live without investigating what we are.*
KIERKEGAARD: *To understand everything except oneself is very comical.*
PLOTINUS: *Our self-knowledge is our beauty: in self-ignorance we are ugly.*

[2]WITTGENSTEIN: *It is not how things are in the world that is mystical, but that it exists.*

[3]PLOTINUS: *He has given Himself existence, He has acted Himself into Being.*

32: SCIENCE-1 OVERCOMES TIME

One of the most telling witnesses to the validity of SCIENCE-3 is the range and accuracy of its predictions, from the precise timing of eclipses and comets to weather-forecasting, from the trajectory of a bullet in a high wind to the minutely detailed programming of a Moon-shot. Surely SCIENCE-1 cannot begin to compete with this. Can the practice of seeing myself here at the world's Centre tell me anything at all about the world's future? Has SCIENCE-1 some secret almanac or crystal ball of its own?

Certainly it can tell me nothing about the future of *others there* - that is the job of SCIENCE-3. But it does tell me everything about the future (and the past) of *Myself here*, of this crystal-clear Reality as distinct from its clouded appearances, this Reality which is in fact everyone's Reality, this Inside Story which is in fact everyone's Inside Story. SCIENCE-1 minds its own business: it makes only one prediction, but that prediction is all-embracing, absolutely precise, plain, infinite in time-range, final, because it is concerned with what things are and not with what they seem to be. And what they are is always the same, the always-so.[1] This Root or Plainness or Core of Sameness is identical in all beings for ever, their Long Home, their Perennial Simplicity. It is in them not merely as the aftertaste of their common Origin and the foretaste of their common Destiny, but as that Origin and that Destiny united and ever-present as their very Being. Seeing this (just understanding it is of no avail) is seeing through time into eternity, now. And this ultimate prediction is the realisation of the Rest and Peace at the common Heart of all creatures.[2]

The alternative is ever-mounting anxiety - the anxiety that grows with intelligence and responsibility and knowledge: in short, with time-range. The further SCIENTIST-3 sees, the more trouble he sees brewing - his own failing powers and sickness and old age and death, global over-population leading to general malnutrition, racial and religious struggles worsening, the cumulative pollution and exhaustion of Earth's natural resources, the eventual burning-out of the Sun involving Earth's slow death, the heat-death or entropy of the Galaxy itself. However the details of the story may vary, the end is the same: everything perishes, and its destruction is the more miserable for being foreseen. Again, SCIENTIST-3 is all too successful - and not nearly successful enough. He falls painfully into time,

74

between the two stools of no time and all time.

What, then, shall one do? Unable to go back to the narrow time-range of the comparatively carefree child, one's only remedy is to go forward to the infinite time-range of the childlike sage, who is wholly carefree because he sees that What he now is lies beyond life and death and all change. Though every-thing perishes the No-thing remains. Appearances are inevitably fleeting; but the Reality they are appearances of, the Mystery they continually arise from - what are a few million galaxies more or less to this inexhaustible Abyss? So it all comes back to the crucial question of my true Identity. If I insist on making an object and a thing and a 3rd person of myself here, I am consumed with a thousand fears and better off dead. But if I give up this unrealistic and unrewarding habit and come to Myself, I see that I have never emerged from that marvellous Abyss, that before Abraham was I am, before the first galaxy and the first atom, before time itself. Right here and now, in the very place all this stormy weather of time and change come from, I am Home and dry. Where can I go from this Safe Haven?

[1]CHUANG-TZU: *All that has form, sound, colour, may be classed under the head* thing. *But one can arrive at formlessness and vanquish death. How can mere* things *compare with what is in possession of the eternal?*

[2]ECKHART: *While man has time and place, number and quantity, he is not as he should be, is not just.*

33. SCIENCE-1 CONTROLS THE ENVIRONMENT

Among all the witnesses in the cause of SCIENCE-3 the chief is its wonderful ability, not only to predict events, but to alter their course and to change the world. After every allowance has been made for all its failures and drawbacks, SCIENCE-3 does make a huge difference, it works wonders, it thoroughly re-creates man's environment. Has SCIENCE-1 anything comparable, anything tangible at all, to show for itself?

Well, there is indeed no hope - or danger - of its adding materially to the achievements of SCIENCE-3. It has quite other work to do, work which doesn't make some not-always-intentional and not-always-beneficial difference to this very small corner of the universe, but all the difference to all of it. *For everything, when viewed simultaneously with its Viewer, thing to No-thing, is radically changed thereby.* True, there's a sense in which nothing is changed: the sky isn't much bluer or greyer, some people remain less agreeable than others, the cold wind still blows through me: indeed, I find myself more and not less coolly realistic about the good and the bad and the indifferent, the beautiful and the ugly and the plain dull. Yet in another and much more important sense everything is changed - and not merely for the better, but actually perfected. This is because it is no longer outside me and alien and therefore a potential or actual threat, but instead is from me and in me, is mine, is profoundly Myself, and therefore all of it acceptable and even - in the end - intentional. In religious terms, my whole-hearted acceptance of God's will (as expressed in how things are) is the alignment of my will with his until what he wants I want, and my total impotence and surrender and his omnipotence become the same thing.[1] This paradox amounts to self-deception, if not nonsense, till it is actually tried out. It isn't for taking on trust but for testing - by the sincere and sustained practice of two-way looking, observing seer and seen simultaneously, *and noticing what happens to the seen.* Those who have carried out the test thoroughly claim that the environment is really controlled and made over till Earth is revealed as Heaven itself.

[1]DE CAUSSADE: *Sanctity consists in willing what happens to us by God's order. If we understood how to see in each moment some manifestation*

of the will of God we should find therein also all that our hearts could desire.
RABBI NAHMAN OF BRATZLAV: *Others gain authority over you if you possess a will distinct from God's will.*

34: SCIENCE-1 IS PRACTICAL

At least (it might be argued) SCIENCE-3 is practical in ordinary, down-to-earth terms. It knows how to deal with a knock in the engine or an outbreak of swine-fever, and countless other problems - on all of which SCIENCE-1 is silent.

Obviously so. All the same, if 'practical' means 'altering things for human benefit' then SCIENCE-3 is often very unpractical indeed. There always turns out to be a debit side to its benefits - huge unbudgeted costs, unforeseen side-effects and backwashes which reduce or even cancel the credit balance. Thus mechanical inventions can hardly go on supplementing and replacing human skills, and still leave them intact. Antibiotics promote the rapid evolution of strains of micro-organisms that are resistant to antibiotics. Then there is the notorious instance of over-population resulting from the control of epidemic diseases and from extended medical care and improved medical techniques, along with modern sanitation, famine relief and so on. What could be less 'practical' than the outcome - if it is the survival of millions who would otherwise have succumbed, leading to more food shortage and squalor and disease? Again, pest control, selective weed killers, inorganic fertilisers, and scientific farming generally, though outstandingly 'practical', are clearly not unmixed blessings even now, and their long-term effects are incalculable. And much the same story could be told of every major technical advance. The faster SCIENCE-3 progresses the more numerous and keener the swords of Damocles it suspends over man's head. This may help to keep him on his toes, but it is scarcely a 'practical' way of doing so.

Happily, the 1st Person has no head for swords to descend on. And happily the Science of the 1st Person is unarmed and quite safe; it never hurt anyone; it has no unfortunate side-effects. It does only good, and that good is immense. In a word, it really is *practical* - and practical not merely in that it makes the world a better place for the seer, but for everybody to live in. Though free from any such intention, it is the business of SCIENCE-1 to save the world from the consequences of SCIENCE-3. The current headaches - war, racial conflict, economic greed, the generation gap, crime and violence, mental illness, drug addiction, with all the other symptoms of mankind's basic anxiety - come from thinking one has a head to ache, that one is what one isn't, a thing or 3rd person. And everyone who is cured of this insane delusion automatically helps to cure others, and so does far more towards the world's amelioration than the world could begin to suspect. This is being really practical.

As for practicality nearer home, I notice that when I come to myself and recognise Who I am, I work and play much better, with more energy and zest and enjoyment, more creatively: what I do I tend to do well, lovingly, effectively. What could be more down-to-earth than this? And what could be less down-to-earth than pretending to be what I'm not - as if I could safely and usefully wield a saw while supposing it was a hammer! Truly my behaviour is never so irresponsible and airy-fairy as when I dismiss the Void that I am right here - this Primary Producer which could hardly be accused of impracticality, seeing that it manufactures and delivers out of its own Emptiness this work-able universe (plus, for good measure, its own delighted aware-ness of doing so): the whole contraption put together on the strict do-it-yourself principle, but without any raw materials or toolkit or instruction booklet, or any outside help whatever! To put it mildly, the 1st Person - and the Science of the 1st Person - are business-like. They deliver the goods.[1]

The basic impracticality and nonsense, to which one is so prone, is in fact duplex. Attributing 3rd personhood to this 1st Person as such, and 1st Personhood to those 3rd persons as such - bunging myself up and spooking them up - are two sides of a coin. It's a counterfeit coin, which the Mayor of Glastonbury[2] (of all fictional characters the most realistic) recognised as worthless. "He was obsessed with a trance-like absorption of interest by the appearance of our world *exactly as it appeared*... People's thoughts were non-existent to the Mayor of Glastonbury; and if there is a level of possibility more non-existent than non-existence itself, such a level was filled (for him) by people's instincts, feelings, impulses, aspirations, intuitions... In his dealings with his fellow citizens upon the town council the Mayor held his own very well. He did this by the enormous advantage he possessed over people who believed in the reality of thoughts and feelings. Sometimes when a thief or a liar came into conflict with him the offender was bewildered by the Mayor's penetration." Add to all this the fact that he was (according to his author) a happy man and a good citizen, and you must agree that he was also eminently practical.[3]

---

[1]ANGELUS SILESIUS: *God is a wondrous thing:*
                          he wills that which he is
                    And is that which he wills
                          with no end or cause.

[2]I quote from *A Glastonbury Romance*, by John Cowper Powys, pp. 212 ff., New York, 1932.

[3]BAYAZID OF BISTUN: *I looked and saw that all created things were dead. I pronounced four akbirs over them and returned from the funeral of them all, and without intrusion of creatures, through God's help alone, I attained unto God.*

35: SCIENCE-1 IS SPONTANEOUSLY APPLIED

SCIENCE-3 goes deeply into the things that make up the world, forcing them to give up their hidden secrets - secrets which are then, after lengthy trial and error, and sometimes severe moral struggle, put to every kind of use and misuse.

SCIENCE-1 goes deeper still, to the very Heart of things, and uncovers the central Secret itself, which alone is wholly practical and incapable of abuse or misapplication, and is also put into immediate effect. For here is no time-lag, no nervous and tentative testing and trying out, no anxious deliberation or crisis of conscience, no ethical doubts and discrepancies, intervening between pure science and applied science: the application is instant and appropriate. I find that, when I am seeing clearly Who's seeing, it is unnecessary - it is fatal to that seeing - to worry about what to say or do, to think or feel: the fitting expression of 1st-Personhood occurs as a matter of course, spontaneously, according to circumstances. The outcome is unpredictable. If it proves unconventional, crazy, shocking, or even wicked by local 3rd-person standards, this can't be helped. In the long run, it is what's needed. I know how to wait, but cease dithering. When they are really required, the right things are done. So I don't resolve in advance not to be unloving and mean and petty and irritable, not to boast, over-eat, steal, flatter, despise, fret, sulk (the list is endless), though it may well turn out that such behaviour doesn't occur when I'm attentive to the Source of all behaviour. If I'm observed to be living up to any 'principles', this is an incidental and external view, for the One here is innocent of principles - and everything else. Nor is this the substitution of the Law of Love for the Ten Commandments. The Void here, which is the Source not only of love but its opposite, knows no law. The 1st Person is a-moral, a-everything. Inevitably, for to *prescribe rules to* myself is to make a case of myself, to cultivate a face or self-image, to box myself, to become a memory, a 3rd person, a separate thing that is naturally selfish. And, conversely, to *be Myself* is to be this 1st Person singular who, as consciously identical with all other 1st Persons (not that there are such), is naturally 'unselfish', and whose 'goodness' owes nothing to rules and is truly creative. Rules belong to the world of separate 3rd persons - where, however, they do little to close the gap between man's good intentions and ideas on the one hand, and his behaviour on the other. The tragic discrepancy between the ideal and the actual, between knowing and doing, between the discoveries of SCIENCE-3 and their use, is resolved only by SCIENCE-1 - by discovering the Fountainhead both of knowing and doing.[1]

How can I help others to this discovery? By giving up any such idea, and attending to the Place where there are no others. So long as This is clearly seen, it doesn't matter how inept and confused my expression of it may seem; the point will get across all the same. The only way I can help profoundly is to mind my own profoundest business, now: to see - and see what happens.

[1]D. T. SUZUKI: *With the removal of the 'I' illusion... this one will act with utmost freedom, with fearlessness, like the Dharma-King himself, indeed as the One.*
ST. PAUL: *Where the spirit of the Lord is, there is liberty.*

36: SCIENCE-1 IS BASIC PSYCHOTHERAPY

Nowadays one of the most prolific branches of SCIENCE-3 is psychology, the science of the mind, and in particular psychiatry and psychotherapy, the treatment of the sick mind. Everything about it flourishes - the variety of schools and theories and techniques, the polemic between schools, the discoveries, the jargon, the literature, the popular interest, the number of practitioners, the number of patients - everything flourishes: perhaps even the therapeutic results, which however lag further and further behind the clinical need. Is this department of SCIENCE-3 (some would say no science but an art, or not so much an art as a heavy - or top-heavy - industry) perhaps too creative, so that the more there is of it the more there needs to be? It's as though the psyche's appetite for attention grows with feeding, and that, like a naughty child, it will do anything to get noticed: so it comes up with endless new problems - urgent, lurid, plausible - just to keep laymen alarmed and psychiatrists busy.

SCIENCE-1 has a short way with this problem child: it declines to play that game. And quite properly, for it is the science of the unchanging Subject, not of that protean and chameleon-like pseudo-object called the psyche. It is the science of the Experiencer and not of experiences. In old-fashioned terms, it is the science of Spirit as distinguished from mind and body. The 1st Person, as such, has neither a psyche nor a psychology, but is simple Awareness without a shadow of anything to call its own. Here, I let go of everything. All that I tried to clutch to myself is unloaded upon the world. And now that I find myself here at Centre devoid of all qualities and functions and the world there full of them, I cease labelling some of them 'mental' or 'subjective' or 'secondary' and *mine,* and the rest 'physical' or 'objective' or 'primary' and *not mine.* I find all experience to have external reference, to be centrifugal, so that if I have a mind at all it is none other than my universe. All this lurking mind-stuff makes for and adheres to its objects, leaving the Subject here shot of it all, intrinsically mindless, free, detached, cool.

Thus to disperse the mind is to heal it. It is because SCIENCE-1 is so non-psychological (or meta-psychological) that it is so psychologically effective. It cures my mind by curing me of mind.[1] For, basically, the trouble with my mind is the conviction I've got one; and returning it to store (to the Universe at large or, in Zen terms, to 'Great Space' or the 'One Mind') is enough to set it in order. Clearing up my psychological problems is clearing away my psychology - this imaginary tangle of thoughts and feelings all torn from what they are thoughts and feelings about, and collected together here and shut up in a tiny bone box - the biggest colony of bats in the smallest of belfries. While I'm seeing What I really am as 1st Person I'm clear-headed and clear-minded and clear of body and mind at all levels, with their attendant problems. And while I'm not seeing this I have plenty of problems, all of which are reducible to the problem of this morbid growth called brain/head/mind, this malignancy flourishing right here at the mid-point of my universe. To say that this wen-like cancer gets in my way and blocks my light is an understatement. It maddens me, and not less so for being quite imaginary. This isn't so much *having* mental trouble as gratuitously *making* trouble for myself, at the one Spot which needs to be trouble-free - and manifestly *is* trouble free, whenever I attend to it. Enlightenment, which is shining the light steadily upon this obstructionless Spot, isn't something I can manage without.

Basically, my cure is that I'm relieved of all this psychological stuff. But - for good measure - the stuff itself is vastly improved by letting it go. When 'I'm in love with her' becomes 'She's wonderful', wallowing sentimentality becomes true love. When 'I hate him' becomes 'He's horrible', he isn't so horrible after all but rather disadvantaged. When 'I'm scared' becomes 'He's fierce' inhibiting fear becomes necessary prudence. When 'I have faith' becomes 'God is', I grow truly religious. When 'I'm having a wonderful time' becomes 'What a scene!', the scene changes for the better. When 'My face is plain' becomes 'That face in the mirror is plain', plain Jane grows less plain. When 'I'm enjoying this picture' becomes 'Wow!', the art gallery becomes worth visiting. When 'I'm studying history' becomes 'What happened?', I'm much more likely to remember what happened. And so on. Despoiling the universe of its qualities, I spoil the universe; restoring them, I repair the damage. My little mind explodes into what it has always been - the world unfallen and undivided. When I am consciously at large - no longer a thing among things, a consciousness among consciousnesses - I am Liberated, and the world, in spite of everything, is all right because it is all me.[2] There are no fates, factors, or forces outside the 1st Person that I am, working against me. Even the "nastiest" things

84

that happen to me as 3rd person are in reality my profound intention as 1st Person. So I say YES! to life, and this is the true therapy.

An (adapted) ancient myth brings out the difference between the psychological method of SCIENCE-3 and the meta-psychological method of SCIENCE-1. At the bottom of a lake lives the dragon who guards the Pearl of Enlightenment. SCIENTIST-3 dives in and goes bald-headed for the dragon, who always seems about to give in but never does so, and on no account surrenders his precious jewel. SCIENTIST-1, meantime, quietly edges past the dragon and snatches the Pearl, which he then discovers to be a dragon-taming charm. For, possessed of this infinite Treasure - seeing himself as that Treasure - he doesn't ignore the dragon. Quite the contrary; at last he can face the dragon's endless cavortings fearlessly, objectively, no longer identifying with any part of them. Truly the dragon isn't a dragon any more, but neither is he turned into a pussycat, overnight. Indeed his first reaction to losing his Pearl can be a great show of fury. But all this is foam and froth. The Reality of the dragon, his Source, the only ultimate Power is the Pearl itself, namely the 1st Person singular, present tense.

In plain language, my psychological problems all boil down to the problem of my Identity. They are settled only by attending to the One here, to this 1st Person who is supposed to have them. Here is the only profound analysis, the only therapy which penetrates to the Root of the trouble, the only lasting cure of my disease. Though the results may be slow to manifest (and then be more manifest to others than to me), this way is economical, thorough, foolproof, well-tested over thousands of years, instantly available, and (though in a sense it costs the Earth) quite *gratis*. Freedom is free.

---

[1]*Mind control,* says RAMANA MAHARSHI, *is discovering the mind doesn't exist.* The essential Zen teaching is the 'Doctrine of No-Mind', and Zen's summary way of pacifying my mind is to challenge me to produce it or pin it down or locate it. Thus HUI-CHUNG: *Buddhahood is attained when there is no mind to be used for the task.* And HUANG-PO: *Only have no mind of any kind: this is undefiled knowledge.* Among psychologists themselves there are of course those who reduce mind to behaviour, and Dr Maudsley who wrote: *It might be*

instructive, and not a little startling, to enquire how much meaning is left in the descriptive terms of psychology when all the physical meaning is taken out of them.

[2]ABRAHAM H. MASLOW: *As he gets to be more purely and singly himself ... the astronomer is 'out there' with the stars, rather than a separateness peering across an abyss at another separateness through a telescopic keyhole.*

HERACLEITUS: *Our souls live in the surrounding world.*

CHUANG-TZU: *When Pu-liang Yi put the world and all things and all life outside himself, he achieved the brightness of dawn and could see his aloneness.*

37: SCIENCE-1 DIAGNOSES AND TREATS THE SPECIFIC DISEASE OF MAN

SCIENCE-3 labels 'normal' (mature, adult, sane) those who lose their 1st-Personhood, and 'abnormal' (retarded, infantile, perhaps sick) those who retain it. SCIENCE-1 defines as 'normal' or 'sane' anyone who is consciously both 1st-Person and 3rd, without confusing them.

Until I come to my senses, I try to get face-to-face with everyone I meet and achieve symmetry at all costs. This determination to mix the immiscibles, to adulterate spirit here (at this end of the tunnel) with matter, and matter there (at that end) with spirit, to turn this 1st Person into 3rd and that 3rd person into 1st, to overlay this consciousness with a surface and undermine that surface with a consciousness - this is the age-old, universal psychosis of man.[1] The 'normal' human condition is pathological. Here is a derangement more profound, more insidiously far-reaching, more infectious, more endemic than any other sort of craziness. The difference between my believing I am one thing rather than another (say Napoleon or a teapot instead of Douglas Harding) is negligible compared with the difference between my believing I am any kind of *thing* and my seeing I am *No-thing*. It isn't that the 1st Person and the 3rd are unlike, but that they cannot be compared. They share no common ground. Whatever is true of one is untrue of the other. That is why to confuse them is so damaging.[2]

Four stages of the aetiology and treatment of this disease can be distinguished:

1 Like any animal, the new-born infant is - for himself - Nothing, faceless and at large, unseparate from his world, 1st-Person without knowing it.

2 The young child, becoming briefly and intermittently awareof himself-as-he-is-for-himself, may ask his mother why she has a head and he hasn't, or may protest that he isn't a boy (he's not at all like that child over there in the mirror!), or may even announce that he's nothing, absent, invisible. Yet he's also becoming increasingly aware of himself-as-he-is-for-others - a very human and special 3rd person complete with head and face. Both views of himself are valid and needful.

3 But as the child grows up his acquired view of himself-

from-outside comes to overshadow, and in the end to obliterate, his native view of himself-from-inside. In fact, he grows *down*. At first he contained his world; now it contains him - what little there is of him. He takes everybody's word for what it's like where he is, except his own, and is 1st-Person no longer. The consequences are increasingly miserable. Shrunk from being the Whole into being this contemptible part, he grows greedy, hating, fearful, closed in, and tired. Greedy, as he tries to regain at whatever cost a little of his lost empire; hating, as he tries to revenge himself on a society that has cruelly cut him down to size; fearful, as he sees himself a mere thing up against all other things; closed in, because it is the nature of a thing to keep others out; tired, because so much energy goes in keeping up this thing's appearances instead of letting them go to where they belong. And all these troubles arise from his basic trouble, his identity-delusion, as he imagines (contrary to all the evidence) that he is at 0 feet what he looks like at 6 feet - a solid, opaque, coloured, outlined lump of thingness. In short, he is beside himself, eccentric, self-alienated: so all goes wrong.

4 You, dear Reader, have actually seen, courtesy of my tunnel and your bathroom mirror, what it is to be 1st-Person singular - the No-thing that is nevertheless keenly aware of itself as the Container or Ground of whatever's currently on display. That was some little time ago. I must ask you, now we have got to the end of this book, to go back to the middle of it and repeat that crucial experiment, seeing what you see in the tunnel instead of what you are told to see. This seeing is believing. Altogether unmystical (in the popular sense), it is a precise, total, all-or-nothing experience admitting of no degrees. Relief is instant and complete - so long as it lasts. But now the really exacting part of the work begins: you have to go on seeing your Absence/presence whenever and wherever you can, till the seeing becomes quite natural (repeat *natural*) and unbroken. This is neither to lose yourself in your Emptiness nor in what fills it, but *simultaneously* to view the thing you are looking at and the No-thing you are looking out of. There will be found no times when this two-way attention is out of place or can safely be dispensed with. The price of sanity is vigilance.

The initial seeing is simplicity itself: once noticed, Nothing is so obvious! But it is operative only in so far as it is practised. The results - including freedom from greed, hate, fear, delusion - are assured only while the Absence here, which is Freedom itself, is being attended to.

Since it has in fact happened, one may suppose the 'psycho-sis' of the Species to have been a necessary step in the devious evolutionary process, a recoil in order to make the great forward leap. Doubtless this astonishing lapse had to intervene, the lapse between the unconscious sanity of the animal and the infant (what living thing other than man ever saw itself as a thing?) and the conscious sanity of the Seer. Delusion, after all, plays its part. How could the Absence of everything here be vividly seen if the presence of something here had never been vaguely imagined?

Anyhow, this conscious sanity, or Enlightenment, has been breaking out here and there in the human race for the past 4,000 years, and is at last becoming less rare.[3] It could be exploding, in spite of society's immense resistances. This is fortunate, for the race's survival - let alone cure - may well depend upon conscious 1st-Personhood becoming, though far from universal, at least the recognised norm, against which true mental health is measured. The future doesn't hang upon some *change* in man, but upon his *re-location:* upon the ever-renewed discovery that as 3rd person he belongs at the far end of the tunnel, and as 1st Person at the near end. And that the contrast between them is total.[4]

[1]DICKENS: Mr Dorrit employs the formidable Mrs General to help innocent Miss Dorrit *cultivate a surface.*

[2]ECKHART: *The inward and the outward man are as different as earth from heaven.*
TE-SHAN HSUAN-CHIOU: *Only when you find no things in your mind and find Mind in no things, are you empty and spiritual, formless and marvellous.*

[3]This doesn't mean that one sees oneself, now consciously 1st-Person, as one of the few sane inmates of the human madhouse - on the staff, treating patients! Thinghood is a disease of the 1st Person singular, not of 3rd persons. Another name for SCIENTIST-1 is the Bodhisattva who (says the *Diamond Sutra*) devotes himself to the Enlightenment of all conscious beings - but if he thinks there are separate consciousnesses to be Enlightened, he isn't a Boddhisattva!

[4]EMERSON: *Take the way from man, not to man.*

EPILOGUE

The way things are, there have to be two kinds of science - to take care of the two kinds of 'things' that are. These two kinds are variously named Oneself and others, the Faceless and the faced, Subject and object, Observer and observed, 1st Person and 3rd; and they lie at an angle of 180° to each other and there is no similarity between them at all. That is why SCIENCE-1, as we have seen, is nothing like SCIENCE-3. Nevertheless, and just because they are polar opposites, SCIENCE-1 has no quarrel with its opposite number, but is (on the contrary) its necessary counterpart and fulfilment, resolving its built-in contradictions and furnishing one multi-purpose solution to all the major practical and theoretical problems it poses. The evidence for this statement has, for brevity's sake, been presented somewhat dogmatically in the foregoing 37 Sections, but in fact it is meant for moment-to-moment testing and never for taking on trust. To be exact, it can't be taken on trust anyway: only when one ceases to make a 3rd person or thing of oneself, only when one isn't playing the Face Game, does the science of 1st-Personhood mean anything. And then it needs no proving. So long as one is seeing how it is here, one is the sole and final authority on This, and even the present essay is wide of the mark - by about twelve inches. It can do no more than point to What is, at this very moment, in front of these very words, reading them.